Vast, Intricate Machines Click

faultlessly through their electronic paces, echoing the tempo of a highly technical age.

These manufactured "brains" maintain inventories, calculate payrolls, keep track of plane reservations, guide missiles, play games, compose music, translate. Thousands of people are influenced by their work, but only a handful of people understand *how* they work. The technical literature is almost unintelligible to the layman.

In this fascinating book, Irving Adler explains the theory of computers in terms that can be easily understood by anyone who has had elementary algebra. He begins with the simplest mathematical concepts—everyday arithmetic, the binary scale of numerals, the brief essentials of logic, showing how these concepts are used in the building of mechanical calculators. From this, he takes the reader into the algebra of classes, propositions, and switching circuits. Finally he illustrates how Boolean algebra is used to design circuits that can calculate and perform deductive reasoning.

Here is a book that unveils a modern mystery, that explains how the art of mathematics engendered great mathematical brains which can think faster than man, calculate more accurately, and follow a process of logic without any of the fallibility of human thought.

Other SIGNET SCIENCE LIBRARY BOOKS

Irving Adler

THINKING
MACHINES

*A Layman's Introduction to
Logic, Boolean Algebra and
Computers*

With diagrams by Ruth Adler

 A Signet Science Library Book

Published by THE NEW AMERICAN LIBRARY

Published as a SIGNET SCIENCE LIBRARY BOOK
By Arrangement with The John Day Company, Inc.

FIRST PRINTING, FEBRUARY, 1962

SIGNET TRADEMARK REG. U.S. PAT. OFF. AND FOREIGN COUNTRIES
REGISTERED TRADEMARK——MARCA REGISTRADA
HECHO EN CHICAGO, U.S.A.

SIGNET SCIENCE LIBRARY BOOKS are published by
The New American Library of World Literature, Inc.
501 Madison Avenue, New York 22, New York

PRINTED IN THE UNITED STATES OF AMERICA

Contents

THINKING MACHINES

CHAPTER 1

Hardware Brains

WE HAVE entered the age of "thinking" machines and automation. Organized collections of hardware, made mostly of metal and glass, carry out activities that used to be the monopoly of the living human brain. They make long and involved calculations, weigh possible courses of action in complex situations, and exercise functions of guidance and control. What is more, they do these things faster and more accurately than the unaided brain can do them.

Electronic Clerks

In the simplest jobs that they do, electronic "brains" serve as clerks and bookkeepers. In many offices, factories and stores, they maintain inventories of supplies. In railroad and airline offices they keep track of ticket sales and reservations. In these activities, the computers operate at their lowest levels of skill. They add and subtract numbers, and store the results in their "memory" devices. They get more of a chance to show their powers when they are put to work calculating payrolls. Using stored information about rates of pay, number of hours worked, social security tax rates, and rules for withholding-tax deductions, they calculate the paychecks of individual workers. In these calculations they use all the basic operations of arithmetic: addition, subtraction, multiplication and division.

Guides for Missiles

Firing a missile at a moving target is no simple matter. The path of the missile depends on more than the speed and direction with which it is launched. From the moment the missile leaves the ground it is pulled by gravity, blown by the wind, held back by air resistance, and turned by the rotation of the earth. All these factors must be taken into account when the path of the missile is calculated. Of the many possible paths that the missile may be given, one must be selected that allows it to intercept the moving target. The calculations needed to make this selection are carried out before the missile is fired. In the case of a guided missile, there are more calculations made after the missile is fired. The path that the missile follows is compared with the path that it should follow. As fast as errors in the path are detected, the course of the missile is altered to make up for them. Only electronic computers work fast enough to make these corrections while the missile is in flight. The computers that plot and correct the path of a missile do more advanced mathematics than those that merely keep inventory or calculate payrolls. They solve what are known as *differential equations*.

The Robot That Beats Its Master

In order to show what a computer can do, and to help explore new areas of activity for computers, the companies that make them have designed some that play games. One of these was wired to play a good game of checkers against a human opponent. The machine looks ahead several moves. It examines all the moves that it may make, and all the possible countermoves of its opponent. After weighing all the possibilities, it chooses the move that seems to be best. The machine remembers every move of every game, so that in future games it may avoid the moves that didn't work out so well. In other words, this machine "learns" from its own mistakes. Because of this built-in ability to learn, the machine has improved its game so much that it now plays checkers better than the engineer who designed its circuit.

Factories without People

In an ordinary factory, there are machines that do much of the work, but there are men and women who control the operation of the machines. In an automated factory these men and women are displaced, because even the job of control is taken over by machines. So far, automation has proceeded the furthest in the oil and chemical industries. There is a continuous flow of materials moving and being changed according to a definite plan. Measuring instruments at key stages of the process report the temperature, pressure, rate of flow, and other relevant measurements. If any of these measurements is not what it should be, the machine that is in control of the process immediately takes the steps needed to make a correction. For example, if one of the materials is flowing in too slowly, a valve is opened to permit it to flow faster. If it is flowing in too fast, a valve is partly closed to slow it down.

Composers and Translators

The variety of jobs that computers can do increases from day to day. When a giant radio telescope tunes in on the messages sent from a rocket in interplanetary space a computer guides the turning of the telescope to make it face in the right direction. There are computers that can play chess, and computers that compose simple songs. Some computers are pilots that guide ships. Others are language specialists that translate books and magazine articles from one language into another.

The Thinking of a Computer

We refer to automatic computers as "thinking machines" or "electronic brains." These terms are dramatic, but not very accurate. They make it seem as though the computers can do the same kind of thinking that the human brain can do. Actually, this is not so. Roughly speaking, there are two kinds of human thinking. There is *creative* thinking, based on imagination and insight. This is the thinking displayed in its highest form by a Beethoven when he composes a symphony, a Shakespeare when he writes a play, or an Einstein when he formulates a new scientific theory. This kind of thinking follows unpredictable channels, and follows no fixed rules. There is also routine thinking, that requires no special talent to carry it out. It proceeds according to fixed rules along a course that is easily foreseen. Any school boy who knows the rules can think out a sum in arithmetic, can solve a quadratic equation, or can translate a paragraph of simple French. It is only this kind of routine thinking that a so-called "thinking machine" can do. The fact that it is routine thinking, however, does not make it unimportant. A large part of the thinking we do in our daily lives is of this routine type. And often, while it is routine, it is also complex and time-consuming. We save a lot of time and energy, and avoid many errors, by letting the machine take this thinking off our hands, or rather, off our minds. Moreover, it is no routine matter to design a machine that can do routine thinking. Behind the routine thinking of the machine is the creative thinking of the men who invented it.

The thinking machine is one of the great marvels of the twentieth century. How do we succeed in making it think? To answer this question we must first answer two other questions. What is a machine? And, what is the nature of the routine thinking that we are turning over to the machines? These questions are explored in the chapters that follow.

CHAPTER 2

Tools with Self-Control

Extensions of the Body

THINKING machines are tools of a special kind. Like other tools, they serve as inanimate extensions of the human body. Hammers are extensions of the hand; they increase the force with which the hand can strike a blow. Tweezers are also extensions of the hand; they reduce the force with which we grasp things, so that we can handle small and delicate objects without crushing them. Telescopes and microscopes are extensions of the eye. Telephones are extensions of the ear. Automobiles and railroad trains are extensions of our legs. Similarly, thinking machines are inanimate extensions of the human brain.

The Evolution of Tools

The tools we use have gone through three stages of evolution. The first stage is that of the hand tool. The hand tool is specially designed to do one or more specific jobs. A hammer, for example, can drive a nail in. It may also have a claw for pulling nails out. But a hand tool does not do its work alone. A human muscle must wield the tool, and a human brain controls the muscle.

The second stage is that of the power tool. This is the stage that is usually meant when we use the word "ma-

14

chine." In this stage the human muscle has been replaced by an engine, an inanimate source of power. But the tool and the engine that moves it are still guided by the human brain. Often the power tool is capable of performing several distinct operations. It may be set to carry out all these operations in a fixed sequence. Or it may perform different operations chosen for different occasions. But the choice is always made in the brain of the person who operates the tool.

The third stage is that of the automatic machine. The main feature of the automatic machine is that it is a machine *with self-control*. If it performs only one operation, it decides for itself when to start or stop. If it can perform many different operations, it decides for itself which ones to do, and in what order to do them. These decisions are not free decisions. They are made according to fixed rules that are built into the working of the machine. In this stage, the built-in control mechanism has taken over the guidance function formerly exercised by the human brain. It operates as an inanimate extension of the brain. All machines that are referred to as "thinking machines" are tools in this third stage of development.

Here is a simple example of the evolution of a tool passing through all three stages of development: Assume that the heat for a room is supplied by an oil burner. Suppose we form a closed circuit of the oil burner and a voltage supply, and then break the circuit by cutting one of the connecting wires. We can close the circuit again and turn on the oil burner by grasping the cut ends of wire, one in each hand, and pressing them together. This is not a wise way of doing it, even if the wires are insulated, because there is the danger of getting an electric shock. A better way of doing it is to connect the two ends of wire to the terminals of a toggle switch. Then we can close the circuit by throwing the switch. The switch is a tool that takes over from our hands the job of closing the circuit. It is a hand tool because we use the muscles of our hand to make it work. We can convert it into a power tool by attaching a clock to it, so that the clock closes the switch in the morning to turn the oil burner on, and opens it at night to turn the oil burner off. Finally, we can convert the switch into an automatic tool by introducing a thermostat. Then the thermostat has control of the switch that turns the oil burner on or off. The thermostat "decides" to turn the oil burner on when the room is too cool. It "decides" to turn the oil burner off again when the room is warm. It makes these decisions because of the way in which it is constructed. One of the contact points of the switch is mounted on a thin bar made of two sheets of metal that are joined back to back. Each sheet of metal expands when it warms up, and contracts when it cools. But they expand and contract at different rates. As a result, when the bar grows warmer it curls and pulls the contact points of the switch apart. Then the switch is opened and the oil burner is turned off. Later, if the bar has cooled sufficiently, it straightens out again. The contact points are brought together until they touch. Then the switch is closed, and the oil burner is turned on. A thermostat switch is an automatic tool because it has this built-in self-control.

Controlling a Car

To understand what is required to give a machine self-control, let us examine another familiar situation, that of driving an automobile. Consider first the actions of a person who is learning how to drive. His instructor sits at his side and tells him what to do. After he starts up in first, the instructor says, "Take your foot off the gas. Step on the clutch and shift into second. Let out the clutch slowly, and step on the gas." Later, as they cruise in traffic, the instructor may say, "You are getting too close to the car ahead of you. Step on your brake gently." Under these conditions, who is in control of the car? Obviously, it is the instructor, and not the driver. The instructor is making all the decisions. His instructions are signals that activate the movements of the driver. The driver does not control the car until, after having acquired experience, he begins to make his own decisions and give himself the signals that activate his movements. The experienced driver hears the sound of his engine as he starts up in first, and sees his car picking up speed. He recognizes when to shift into second

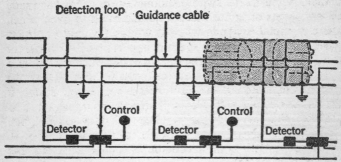

Automatic control of auto traffic

from what he hears and sees and feels. *The basis of his control of the car is the fact that he observes the results of his own actions, and these observations become signals that initiate his next actions.* When a mechanism can detect the results of its action, and is guided by these results, engineers say that it has *feedback*. Now, if we can build a feedback system into the car itself, we can dispense with the driver, and have a car that controls itself. A step in this direction has already been taken by General Motors and the Radio Corporation of America. They have developed a system for automatic control of a car that is riding on a highway. The car detects the results of its own movements through an electronic feedback system built into the roadway and the car. A guidance cable in the roadway warns the car when it is straying from its lane. Detection loops in the roadway sense the presence of other cars ahead. If the car gets too close to a preceding car, the feedback system puts on the car's brake to slow it down.

The Key to Self-Control

Feedback is the key to self-control. To make a machine automatic, we have to provide it with a feedback mechanism. This means we must provide it with a means of observing the results of its own actions. Each type of result has to generate a distinct signal. The action of the machine has to be guided by these signals according to a predetermined plan.

Automatic Calculators

The term "thinking machine" is used most often to refer to automatic calculators. These machines "think" in a double sense. First, as tools that carry out computations, they serve as extensions of the brain. Secondly, as automatic tools, they carry out the guidance function formerly supplied by the brain. These two types of thinking are distinct, and are carried out by separate parts of an electronic brain. One part is a calculator, that can do arithmetic when it is told what to do. The other part is the control unit, that tells the calculator what to do.

CHAPTER 3

Getting an Idiot to Think

Making the Complicated Simple

A TYPICAL tool can carry out only a few easy operations. A calculating machine is like other tools in this respect. It moves in certain predetermined ways. These are simple in nature and few in number. The machine is like an idiot that moves only on command, and can understand and follow only a few commands. Nevertheless, we are using such machines for carrying out very complex calculations. We have transformed the idiot into a competent mathematician. How is this transformation accomplished? How do we get a simple machine to carry out a complicated job? We do it by first making the complicated job simple. We break the job down into a sequence of small steps, each of which is simple and is in the range of what the machine is capable of doing. Then we see to it that the machine carries out these steps in the proper sequence.

A familiar example of this procedure is seen in the operation of a knitting machine. Sweaters may be knit in a great variety of complicated patterns. But all of these patterns, no matter how complex, are built up out of sequences of a few simple knitting operations, such as *knit, purl, increase, decrease, slip,* and *yarn over*. The knitting machine is designed to carry out these simple steps. To have the machine knit a complex pattern, we first identify the sequence of steps in the pattern, and then instruct the machine to follow this sequence.

If a machine is electrically operated, its action may be controlled by opening and closing switches. A particular set of switches will control a particular step that the machine can perform. The switches themselves can be opened or closed by electrical signals. By supplying these signals to the machine in a definite sequence, we can get the machine to perform a particular sequence of steps.

When a machine knits a sweater, every step it performs can be charted in advance. Such a machine can be given a single complete set of instructions before it starts working. The situation is somewhat different for a machine that makes calculations. It is not possible to list in advance all the steps it must perform, because some of the later steps depend on the outcome of the earlier steps. For example, if the machine is adding some two-digit numbers, we do not know whether it will have to carry a number to the second column from the sum of the first column until we know what that sum is. To deal with this situation, we give the machine several sets of instructions. Then, we give the machine the general instruction that, after each step it performs, it should observe the outcome of that step and then choose the appropriate instructions for the next step. This is where the feedback mechanism of the machine comes into play.

The Turing Machine

To show concretely how a simple machine can be given the ability to perform complex calculations, we shall describe one designed by the late British mathematician A. M. Turing. Turing's machine is a purely imaginary one. He invented it for theoretical purposes. A working model can easily be made, because hardware is available that can carry out the acts that the machine is required to perform. However, we do not propose that you make a model to see how it works. We suggest, instead, that you cast yourself in the role of the machine. Make believe that you are the machine. Follow blindly the instructions that the machine is given, just as an inanimate mechanical device would. In this way you will get a full appreciation of the nature of the mindless thinking that the machine performs.

The Turing machine has these parts: a tape, divided into squares; a motor, for moving the tape; a scanning device for reading what is written on the tape; a writing device that can write X's or 1's or can erase them; a numbered dial with a pointer; and a control unit that tells the machine what to do. The machine can perform only these simple acts: It can write an X or a 1 in a blank square. It can erase an X or a 1 that is already there. It can move the tape one square to the left or to the right. It can flash an appropriate signal and then stop when its work is done. In a mechanical model, the control unit would be an electronic device that receives signals from the scanner and the dial after each step. These signals would activate switches that initiate the next step the machine should take. For our purposes, the control unit will simply be a table which you can read to obtain the machine's instructions.

In order to play at being the machine, first prepare these pieces of equipment: a pencil, an eraser, a narrow strip of paper divided into squares, a blank sheet of paper, and a card. The blank sheet of paper will be your dial. Write the number 1 on it. When you are instructed to change the dial setting, cross out or erase the number that is there, and write the new dial setting in its place. The card will serve to fix the position of the scanner. Place the tape under the card so that part of the tape is exposed to the right of the card. The first square next to the right edge of the card will be the square that is being scanned.

Numbers are written on the tape in the most primitive possible way, as a sequence of 1's. The X's are used to indicate where a number begins and ends. Let us begin by entering on the tape the numbers 2 and 3, as shown in the drawing below. Place the tape under the card so that the last 1 on the extreme right is in the position of being scanned. This is the starting position for the machine. Now we show how the machine is launched on the job of performing some operation in arithmetic with the numbers that are on the tape. A program for this operation is worked out, and it is embodied in a control table. The table is independent of the numbers that are entered on the tape.

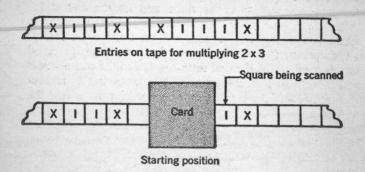

Entries on tape for multiplying 2 x 3

Square being scanned

Starting position

The Turing "machine"

No matter what the numbers may be, the machine need only follow the instructions given by the table, and it will automatically carry out the operation and stop when the job is done. The answer will appear as a single string of 1's on the tape.

The program for doing addition is given in the first control table on page 24. The numbers 1 to 6 in the first column represent dial settings of the machine. The symbols at the top of the table, a blank square, a square with an X, and a square with a 1, represent what the scanner may see. By entering the table in the row indicated by the dial setting, and in the column indicated by what the scanner sees, the machine obtains the instructions it should follow for each step. The instructions are made up of two parts, a letter and a number. The letter may be D, X, E, R, or L. D means write the digit 1 in the square being scanned. X means write an X. E means erase what appears in the square. R means move the tape one square to the right. L means move the tape one square to the left. The number in the instructions means change the dial setting to that number. A question mark in the instruction box means, "What happened? You made a mistake somewhere." An exclamation mark means, "Stop. The job is done." For example, in the starting position, the dial setting is 1, and the scanner sees a 1. So you look for instructions in the row labeled 1, and the column headed 1. The instructions are, "*R*1: Move the tape one square to the right, and set the dial at 1." After these instructions are followed, the dial setting is again 1, and the scanner sees a 1 once more. So the instructions for the second step are the same. After the third step is carried out, the dial setting is 1, and the scanner sees an *X*. Now the instructions are, "*E*2: Erase the *X*, and set the dial at 2." As a result, the dial setting is 2, and the scanner sees a blank square, so the instructions for the fifth step are, "*R*2: Move the tape one square to the right, and set the dial at 2." The reader is advised to continue, following the instructions step by step until the computation is completed. If you have the time and the patience, do another addition example with larger numbers. Remember to begin with the dial set at 1 and the tape in the starting position described above.

The other tables on page 24 give programs for carrying out multiplication and exponentiation (raising to a power). When the exponentiation table is used, the right hand number on the tape is the base, and the left hand number is the exponent. For example, if the numbers 2 and 3 are written as shown on page 22, with the 2 to the left of the 3, then 3 is raised to the second power. To raise 2 to the third power, write the 3 to the left of the 2.

When you work out a complete addition example, you will observe that the machine adds the two numbers written on the tape by combining the two strings of 1's into a single long string. If you use the control table for multiplication, you will see that the machine multiplies by doing repeated addition. Similarly, the machine does exponentiation by doing repeated multiplication. The more complex operations are accomplished through repetition of the simpler ones.

The Turing machine is not a practical calculator. It writes numbers by the laborious method of putting down long strings of 1's. It makes calculations by moving these 1's, one at a time, across lengthy stretches of tape. The

Control Tables for the Turing Machine

Program for Addition

	□	X	1
1	D6	E2	R1
2	R2	E3	?
3	R3	E4	E5
4	L4	?	R6
5	L5	?	R1
6	X6	|	R3

Program for Multiplication

	□	X	1
1	?	R2	R1
2	R2	E3	?
3	R3	E12	E4
4	L4	L5	?
5	?	?	E6
6	L6	L7	L6
7	D8	?	L7
8	L9	R8	R8
9	L9	R10	E6
10	D10	R11	R10
11	R11	E12	E4
12	L12	E13	?
13	L13	L14	E13
14	X15	L14	L14
15		|	

Program for Exponentiation

	□	X	1
1	R2	R1	R1
2	R2	E3	?
3	L3	L4	L4
4	D5	L4	L4
5	X5	R6	L5
6	R7	R6	R6
7	R7	R8	E8
8	L8	L8	E9
9	L9	L10	L9
10	L10	L10	E11
11	L11	L12	L11
12	D13	?	L12
13	L14	R13	R13
14	D15	R15	E11
15	D15	R16	R15
16	L17	R16	R16
17	?	L18	E9
18	?	L18	E19
19	X19	L20	?
20	?	L21	E19
21	X21	R22	L21
22	D23	R22	R22
23	D23	R24	R23
24	R24	E25	E8
25	L25	E26	?
26	L26	E27	E26
27	L27	E27	R28
28	X28	|	

action of a working model would depend on mechanical motion, shifting the tape back and forth one square at a time. For all these reasons, a Turing machine would be too slow to do the calculating jobs described in the first chapter. A really practical calculator would have to meet two major requirements: 1) It would have to have an efficient system for recording numbers. 2) It would have to be able to make computations very quickly. The first requirement is met by using a place-value system of writing numbers. The Arabic numerals that we use every day constitute a place-value system. It is not the only one, however. Of the many possible place-value systems, there is one that is best suited for use by calculating machines. We shall get acquainted with this system in the next chapter. The second requirement is met by building a calculator out of parts that can act without mechanical motion. Machine components that have this property are those made of electronic circuits. The action in them consists of pulses of electric current. Electronic devices can easily generate and manipulate as many as one million pulses per second. Since each pulse corresponds roughly to one step in a simple computation, an electronic calculator can carry out about a million steps in a second. At this rate, even complex calculations that require many steps are carried out at high speed.

The Components of an Automatic Calculator

Although the Turing machine is not a practical calculator, we can learn from it. We find in it all the major components that an automatic calculator should have. When we observe them in action, they suggest questions that should be answered before analogous components can be designed for an electronic calculator.

Every automatic calculator has a *calculating unit* that performs the actual computations. In the Turing machine the calculating unit consisted of the tape that moved back and forth, and the pencil and eraser that entered and removed 1's and X's. The calculating unit took this peculiar form because of the method that was used for writing numbers. So we see that the system employed for writing numbers determines, in part, the design of the calculating unit. Since we shall be using a place-value system for writing numbers, we shall have to look into the question, "How can electronic circuits be designed to represent numbers written in a place-value system, and to carry out computations with them?" To answer this question, we first get acquainted with different ways of writing numbers (Chapter IV) and various devices, both mechanical and electrical, for making calculations (Chapter VI).

Every automatic calculator has a *control unit* that guides the calculating unit through the sequence of steps it performs. In the Turing machine, the control unit gave the instructions that were recorded in the control tables. In an electronic computer, the control unit is itself an electronic device. So we have to look into the question, "How can an electronic device give such instructions to a calculator?" We find additional questions that we should explore when we notice the form that the Turing machine's control system took. The instructions for each step depended on what the dial setting was, and what the scanner saw just before the step was taken. When the machine was doing addition, the dial might be set at 1 *or* 2 *or* 3 *or* 4 *or* 5 *or* 6. The scanner might see a square that was blank, *or* contained a 1, *or* contained an *X*. The table that gave the instructions is essentially a condensed way of writing statements of this form: *If* the dial is set at 2, *and* the square being scanned contains an *X, then* erase the *X and* set the dial at 3. In the sentences above that describe what the dial does, what the scanner sees, and what the control table says, the key words are *or, and, if,* and *then*. These words represent certain logical ideas. We shall have to investigate the part that these ideas play in logical thinking, and then look into the question, "How can we get an electronic circuit to do this kind of thinking?" That is why we take up Logic and Boolean Algebra, and their relationship to circuit design, in Chapters VII, VIII, IX and X.

Every automatic calculator has a *memory unit*. In the Turing machine, the dial was a primitive memory unit. It stored information derived from its earlier steps, when this information was needed to guide its later steps. In an electronic computer, the memory units are electrical or magnetic devices. We shall have to look into the question, "How can these devices store and deliver on demand such things as numbers and instructions for the calculating unit?" This question is taken up in Chapter XI.

Every automatic calculator has an *input unit* and an *out-*

put unit. The input unit supplies to the machine the data it works with, and special instructions for the job to be done. The output unit delivers the results of the machine's calculations. The input and output of the Turing machine were the written symbols on the tape. The form that they take in electronic calculators will be described in Chapter XI.

CHAPTER 4

Numbers and Numerals

ALL THE numbers we use are derived from the natural numbers, the numbers we use for counting. These are the numbers we call *zero, one, two, three,* and so on. To represent these numbers, we use two different kinds of symbols. One kind is the *number name,* which we can say out loud, or which we spell out when we use written words to stand for spoken words. *One, eleven, one hundred,* and *one million* are examples of number names. The other kind of symbol is a *numeral.* It is a written symbol only. When we read it out loud, we really say the *number name* that corresponds to it. 1, 11, 100, and 1,000,000 are examples of numerals. Notice that as you read them you say "One, eleven, one hundred, and one million," which are the corresponding number names.

There are many ways of assigning number names to the natural numbers. In fact, every language has its own set of number names. The number that is called *two* in English is called *deux* in French, *zwei* in German, and so on. Similarly, there are many ways of writing numerals for these numbers. Where we use the numeral 2, the Romans used the letters II, and the ancient Hebrews used the symbol בּ, a letter of the Hebrew alphabet. In this chapter we shall be discussing different systems of numerals. Consequently we may use several different written symbols to stand for the same number. To avoid confusion, let us agree at the same time to use only one number name for each number, the one that it has in the English language. Thus, although we may use different symbols for the number we ordinarily write as 2, we shall always refer to the number by the name *two*, so that there will be no doubt about what number we mean.

An Alphabet for Numbers

The list of natural numbers *zero, one, two, three,* and so on, is endless. Since we want to be able to write a numeral for each of these numbers, we need an infinite collection of numerals. One way of getting such a collection is to assign a different symbol to each number. This way of writing numbers would be analogous to the Chinese way of writing words. In the Chinese language, there is a separate written symbol for each word. In order to learn how to read Chinese, it is necessary to memorize thousands of symbols. We avoid this difficulty in the English language by using a mere twenty-six symbols as an alphabet. Then we build all written words out of these symbols. In the same way, a more efficient system for writing numbers is obtained by using just a few symbols as a kind of alphabet for numbers, which can be put together to form all the numerals.

We may, for example, use as an alphabet for numbers the symbols 0, 1, and +, with their ordinary meanings. Then we can write all numbers above 1 by adding enough 1's. In this system, 1 + 1 would be the numeral for two, 1 + 1 + 1 would be the numeral for three, and so on. This is the system that we used in the Turing machine, except that we omitted the plus signs. Primitive man used the same system when he cut notches on a tree or made scratches on the ground. The system is useful as long as we use only small numbers. It becomes very cumbersome as soon as large numbers are needed. For this reason, the method of repeating 1's was discarded in all parts of the world in favor of better alphabets for numbers.

New alphabets for numbers arose out of the habit of counting things out in groups. Because we have five fingers on each hand, the groups used most often were groups of five or ten. However, groups of twelve, twenty, and sixty have been used by some peoples in various parts of the world. The use of groups for counting suggested that special notations be used for designating the number of things in a group. In most cases, the notation took the form of new symbols. In the Roman system of numerals, for example, five is designated by V, ten is designated by X, and so on. However, in a few systems of numerals, the group number was designated not by a new symbol, but by an old symbol put in a special place. Systems that use this method are called place-value systems. The Arabic system, which we use today, is a place-value system.

Arabic Numerals

In the Arabic system for writing numbers, as we count up from 0, we introduce a new symbol called a *digit* for each number up to 9. Then we start using the fact that we group things by tens. To write the number ten, we write 10, which is an abbreviation for "one group of ten plus no units." Eleven, which is one group of ten plus one unit, is written as 11, and so on. The meaning of a digit in a numeral depends on its position in that numeral. If it is in the first column from the right, it designates a number of ones. In the second column it designates a number of tens. In the third column it designates a number of hundreds. Thus, 325 means 3 hundreds plus 2 tens plus 5 ones. The basic group of the system is the group of ten. The larger groups are all compounded from groups of ten. One hundred is ten times ten. One thousand is ten times ten times ten, and so on. The number *ten* is called the base of the system.

If We Had Eight Fingers

The choice of *ten* as the base of our system of numerals is the result of a biological accident. We happen to have just ten fingers on our hands. If we had eight fingers on our hands it would have been natural for us to use the number eight as the base of a place-value system for writing numbers. In such a system, we would need separate symbols 0, 1, 2, 3, 4, 5, 6, 7 only for the numbers up to 7. To designate the number eight we would write 10, to mean "one group of eight plus no units." Then 11 would mean one group of eight plus one, or nine. 12 would mean ten, etc. In this system, where eight is the base, 10 means *eight,* 100 means *eight times eight,* or sixty-four, 1000 means *eight times eight times eight,* or five hundred twelve, etc.

Once we recognize that a number other than ten may be used as the base for a place-value system, then the way is left open for devising many more place-value systems. Any natural number larger than one may serve as the base for a place-value system of numerals. The number of digits required in the system is equal to the base. In the Arabic system, where the base is ten, we use ten digits, 0, 1, 2, 3, 4, 5, 6, 7, 8, and 9, to stand for the numbers less than ten. In a system with base eight, we need eight digits, 0, 1, 2, 3, 4, 5, 6, and 7, to stand for the numbers less than eight. In a system with base five, we need only five digits, 0, 1, 2, 3, and 4, to stand for the numbers less than five. Then five itself is represented by 10. This should be read as "one-oh." It should not be read as *ten.* The symbol 10 always means the base of the system of numerals. Hence it means *ten* only when the base is ten. It means *eight* when the base is eight. It means *five* when the base is five. It could also mean *two,* if we choose two as the base.

The Binary Scale

We shall now pay particular attention to the place-value system with base two. It is known as the *binary scale* for writing numerals. It is the simplest of all place-value systems because it uses as base the smallest number above one. It requires only two digits, 0 and 1. They are often referred to as *bits,* a contraction of *binary digits.* We have a special interest in the binary scale because binary numerals can be represented easily by means of electrical devices. A lamp, for example, can be used to represent a bit, by letting it stand for 1 when the lamp is on and for 0 when the lamp is off. For this reason, binary numerals are the natural ones to use for work with electronic computers.

In the binary scale, a 1 in the second place from the right stands for *two.* In the third place it stands for *two times two* or four. In the fourth place it stands for *two times two times two,* or eight, and so on. The numbers, one, two, four, eight, sixteen, etc., are called *powers of two.* So a binary numeral really represents a number as a sum of powers of two. For example, 111 means one four plus one two plus one one. 1010 means one eight plus no fours plus one two plus no ones. Therefore it means eight plus two, or ten.

Lazy Man's Arithmetic

Doing computations with binary numerals is a lazy man's dream. There are only a few binary number facts to memorize. For addition: $0 + 0 = 0$; $1 + 0 = 0 + 1 = 1$; $1 + 1 = 10$. For multiplication: $0 \times 0 = 0$; $0 \times 1 = 1 \times 0 = 0$; $1 \times 1 = 1$. These facts are summarized in the following tables:

Addition		
+	0	1
0	0	1
1	1	10

Multiplication		
×	0	1
0	0	0
1	0	1

To do binary arithmetic, follow the ordinary rules of arithmetic, except that you use these tables instead of the base ten tables that you learned in school.

Binary Numerals

To get better acquainted with the binary scale, suppose we write the binary numerals for the numbers from zero to eight. We can use the addition table to help us figure out what these numerals are. Begin by writing 0 for zero. Then proceed by adding 1's, one at a time. Adding 1 to 0, we get $0 + 1 = 1$. Adding 1 to this result, we get $1 + 1 = 10$. To add 1 to 10, first write the addends one over the other. Then add, column by column. The next few additions are written out in the same way. Keep in mind that when you add 1 and 1, since the sum is 10, you put down the 0 and carry the 1 to the next column to the left:

10	11	100	101	110	111
1	1	1	1	1	1
11	100	101	110	111	1000

Then the binary numerals for the numbers from zero to eight are written as follows:

zero	0	three	11	six	110
one	1	four	100	seven	111
two	10	five	101	eight	1000

To acquire facility with binary numerals, the reader is advised to continue adding 1's until he reaches 32.

There are short-cuts that can be used to write any given number in the binary scale. We give two methods, and demonstrate each by using it to write the number *fifty-nine* in the binary scale.*

* For practice exercises, see *Magic House of Numbers*, by the same author, The John Day Company, New York, 1957.

Method I. Decompose the number into powers of two by first subtracting the highest power of two that is not larger than the number. Repeat the process with the remainder, and continue until the remainder is 0 or 1. The highest power of two that is not more than fifty-nine is thirty-two. When we subtract, the remainder is twenty-seven. The highest power of two that is not more than twenty-seven is sixteen. When we subtract, the remainder is eleven. The highest power of two that is not more than eleven is eight. When we subtract, the remainder is three. The highest power of two that is not more than three is two. When we subtract, the remainder is one. Writing the numbers in Arabic numerals (base ten), we can now write 59 as a sum of powers of two as follows: $59 = 32 + 16 + 8 + 2 + 1$. To take into account the powers of two that are missing, we rewrite it in this way: For every power that is present, write 1 times that power. For every power that is missing, write 0 times that power. Then we have $59 = 1 \times 32 + 1 \times 16 + 1 \times 8 + 0 \times 4 + 1 \times 2 + 1 \times 1$. The numbers that multiply the powers of two are the bits we should use to write 50 in the binary scale. So we have 59 (base ten) = 111011 (base two).

Method II. Write the number in Arabic numerals and divide by 2. Write the quotient underneath, and write the remainder, which is 0 or 1, at the side. Then divide the quotient by 2, and record the quotient and remainder. Continue dividing successive quotients by 2 until you get a quotient that is 0 or 1. The successive remainders and the last quotient give you the bits of the binary numeral in reverse order.

Moving a Bit

In a binary numeral, the meaning of each bit depends on its place in the numeral. What happens to the meaning of

```
2 | 50        Remainders
2 | 29  ............ 1      The arrow shows the order
2 | 14  ............ 1      in which you should copy
2 |  7  ............ 0      the bits to write the numeral
2 |  3  ............ 1      from left to right.
     1  ............ 1
```

Converting to binary scale

the bit if it is moved one place to the left? To answer this question, let us start with the bit 1 in the first place on the right. Here it stands for the number *one*. Now move it one place to the left, and fill the place it has vacated with the digit 0. The new number we get is 10, or *two*. If we move the 1 again, we get 100, or *four*. After the next move, we get 1000, or *eight*, and so on. It is clear that when a bit is moved one place to the left, the number it stands for is multiplied by *two*. (Similarly, in the decimal system, when a digit is moved one place to the left, it is multiplied by ten.)

Now take any binary numeral, shift every one of its bits one place to the left. Since the place on the extreme right is left empty when this is done, fill it with a 0. The shifting doubles the meaning of every bit. As a result, it doubles the meaning of the entire numeral. For example, consider the binary numeral 101. The number it stands for is four plus one, or five. When we shift the bits one place to the left, it becomes 1010, which stands for eight plus two, or ten. We shall see later (page 142), how electronic calculators use the shifting of bits as a simple way of multiplying a number by two.

If shifting a bit one place to the left doubles the number that it stands for, then shifting a bit one place to the right divides the number by two. To be able to shift all bits to the right, without losing sight of which bit is in the units place, we put a dot immediately to the right of the units place, just as we do when we write Arabic (decimal or base ten) numerals. Then bits which stand to the right of the dot stand for binary fractions, just as in Arabic numerals they stand for decimal fractions. Thus, in the binary scale, 1. stands for one, 0.1 stands for one half, 0.01 stands for one fourth, and so on. With this notation, we can use binary fractions to represent common fractions, at least approximately, just as we usually employ decimal fractions for the same purpose.

CHAPTER 5

Algebra of Numbers

Basic Operations

IN EVERYDAY arithmetic, we often have occasion to do four different things with natural numbers: we add them, subtract them, multiply them, and divide them. Each of these operations "combines" two given numbers in a special way to obtain a third number called *sum, difference, product* or *quotient,* respectively. When we add two natural numbers, the sum we get is also a natural number. When we multiply two natural numbers, the product is a natural number. To express the fact that we do not have to go outside the natural number system to find the sum or product of any two natural numbers, we say that the natural number system is *closed* under the operations addition and multiplication. We cannot make the same assertion concerning subtraction or division. While we can subtract 2 from 5 in the natural number system, we cannot subtract 5 from 2 in that system. The latter subtraction becomes possible only in an expanded number system that contains the negative integer -3, a number that is outside the natural number system. Similarly, while we can divide 6 by 2 in the natural number system, we cannot divide 2 by 6 in that system. The latter division becomes possible only in an expanded number system that contains the fraction $\frac{1}{3}$, a number that is outside the natural number system. We see, then, that the natural number system is *not closed* under the operations subtraction and division.

Because of this distinction with regard to closure, the operations addition and multiplication are considered the basic operations in the natural number system. They are considered basic for another reason, too: The other operations can be defined in terms of them. The statement "Subtract 2 from 5" really means "Find the natural number which, when *added* to 2 gives 5 as the sum." The statement "Divide 6 by 2" really means "Find the natural number which, when *multiplied* by 2 gives 6 as the product." So all questions involving subtraction and division can be expressed in terms of the basic operations, addition and multiplication. We designate these basic operations by means of the familiar symbols + and ×.

General Statements

We know from the addition table of ordinary arithmetic that $2 + 3 = 3 + 2$. There are many true statements of the same form: $3 + 5 = 5 + 3$, $4 + 9 = 9 + 4$, and so on. In fact, the relationship expressed in these statements is perfectly general, and may be expressed as a rule in these words: Write the sum of two natural numbers. Then write another sum by interchanging the two numbers. The two sums are equal. This rule can be stated in another form: If x stands for any natural number, and y stands for any natural number, then $x + y = y + x$. In this formulation of the rule, the letters x and y serve merely as place holders. They indicate places that may be filled by natural numbers. Letters used as place holders in this way are called *variables*. The use of variables makes it possible for us to state in very brief form general rules like the one we just observed. In the abbreviated statement of the rules it is customary to leave out the prefatory phrase, "If x stands for any natural number, and y stands for any natural number." Although the phrase is omitted, it must be understood as part of the statement of the rule.

The Rules of Arithmetic

The rule we have just observed is important enough to have acquired a name. We call it the *commutative law of addition.* There is an analogous *commutative law of multiplication,* which may be written in this form: $xy = yx$. Here xy is to be read as "x times y." We are using the usual convention of omitting the multiplication sign between variables, to avoid confusing the multiplication sign with the letter x.

Here are some more general rules about natural numbers, expressed by means of variables:

$x + (y + z) = (x + y) + z$. (Associative Law of Addition)

$x (yz) = (xy) z$. (Associative Law of Multiplication)

$x (y + z) = xy + xz$. (Distributive Law)

The associative law of addition merely expresses the familiar fact that when we add three numbers, it doesn't make any difference whether we first add the first and second number and then add in the third number, or first add the second and third number and then add in the first number. It is because of this law that we are sure that adding a column of figures from the bottom up gives the same result as adding it from the top down.

The distributive law merely expresses the fact that the number of objects in a rectangular array is unaltered if the rectangle is decomposed into two rectangles, as in the diagram below:

$3 \cdot 7$ or $3(5 + 2)$ = $3 \cdot 5$ + $3 \cdot 2$

The distributive law

Distinguished Numbers

The number 0 has a peculiar property in relation to addition. When you add 0 to any natural number, that number is unchanged. Using a variable, the rule about 0 takes this brief form: $0 + x = x$. Let us call this rule the Law of Zero.

The number 1 has an analogous property in relation to multiplication. When you multiply any natural number by 1, the number is unchanged: $1x = x$. Let us call this rule the Law of One.

The Algebra of Natural Numbers

We have just observed that the natural number system has these characteristics: 1) It is a collection of elements that is closed under two operations, each of which "combines" any two elements to form a third element in the system. 2) These operations obey the seven laws displayed above: the Commutative Laws, the Associative Laws, the Distributive Law, the Law of Zero, and the Law of One. Any system which is closed under one or more operations that obey laws somewhat like these is said to have an algebraic structure, or, more briefly, an *algebra*. The seven laws we have examined, together with some others we have not mentioned (since we shall have no need for them in this book), are the foundation of the *algebra of natural numbers*.

The Algebra of Integers

The *negative* of a number is defined as the number you must add to it to get 0 as the sum. In the natural number system, a number that has a negative is a rare thing indeed. In fact, the number 0 is the only natural number that has a negative. However, there are other number systems in which numbers that have negatives are the rule rather than the exception. One of these systems is the system of integers, consisting of 0, the positive integers $+1$, $+2$, $+3$, ..., etc., and the negative integers -1, -2, -3, ..., etc. Here every number has a negative. For example, since the sum of $+3$ and -3 is 0, -3 is the negative of $+3$, and $+3$ is the negative of -3. A minus sign is used as the symbol for the words "the negative of," so that if the variable x stands for some integer, then $-x$ stands for the negative of that integer.

The reader will recall from his high school mathematics days that integers can be added and multiplied, and the result in each case is an integer. In other words, the system of integers is closed under the operations addition and multiplication. Moreover, in this system, the same seven laws that we observed in the natural number system are also obeyed. Consequently there is an *algebra of integers,* and these seven laws are among the properties of that algebra. However, because every integer has a negative, the algebra of integers obeys some additional laws that do not apply to the system of natural numbers. Among these are the four laws listed below, which you will recognize as rules that you learned when you studied high school algebra:

$$-(-x) = x. \qquad -(x + y) = (-x) + (-y).$$
$$(-x)(-y) = xy. \quad x(-y) = -(xy).$$

Because of these laws involving negatives, the algebra of integers is different from the algebra of natural numbers, even though they share some common rules.

Other Algebras

We have made these brief comments about the natural number system and the system of integers for two purposes. One purpose is to show that there is more than one algebra or algebraic structure. Then it will not be a surprise when we encounter a new algebraic structure in the chapters on logic. The second purpose is to show what an algebra looks like. Then we shall be prepared to recognize this new structure as an algebra when we see it.*

* For an elementary introduction to algebraic structures, written for the layman, see *The New Mathematics,* by the same author, The John Day Company, New York, 1958.

CHAPTER 6

Calculating Machines

WHAT picture flashes through your mind as you read the title of this chapter? It is likely that you see an electrical desk calculator, with its rows of numbered buttons, and you hear the rhythmic sound it makes as its motor pushes levers and turns wheels. Or you see some long-forgotten newspaper photograph of a giant electronic brain that suggests a radio repairman's nightmare of a radio boiling over out of its case until it fills a whole room. It is not likely that you see simple, homely things like a pair of rulers, or the rows of beads on a baby's play-pen. But it is precisely these homely things that we shall talk about first, because they are both good examples of calculating machines.

A Simple Adding Machine

A pair of foot rulers can be used as an adding machine. The numbers from 1 to 12 are printed on the face of each foot ruler. Every number is next to a line, and it indicates the number of inches in the distance of that line from the left hand edge of the ruler. The number 0 is not printed on the ruler, but it can be understood to refer to the left hand edge itself. We can use the rulers to add any two of these numbers whose sum is not more than twelve. To add the numbers, place one ruler above the other so that the left edge of the upper ruler lies above one of the addends on the lower ruler. Then locate the other addend on the upper ruler. The sum of the two numbers will appear below it. The diagram shows the position of the rulers for adding 2 and 3.

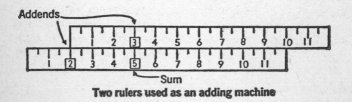

Two rulers used as an adding machine

The Abacus

The rows of beads on a play-pen are part of an *abacus,* an ancient calculating device that is still widely used throughout the world. In its simplest form, each row contains ten beads. In the first row, each bead stands for a unit. In the second row, each bead stands for ten. In the third row, each bead stands for one hundred, etc. The abacus is a place-value system for writing numbers by means of beads. To write the number 325, for example, first begin with all the beads at the left. Then move some beads to the right as follows: 5 beads on the first line to represent 5 units; 2 beads on the second line to represent 2 tens; 3 beads on the third line to represent 3 hundreds.

The number 325 on a simple abacus

To add 117 to this number, move one more bead to the right on the third line, and move one more bead to the right on the second line. We also have to move seven more beads to the right on the first line. We have to do this in two steps. First move as many as we can. After we move five beads, there are no more beads left to be moved. We still have to move two more, however. To provide beads for this purpose, we move the ten beads on the top line back and move another bead on the second line over to the right to take their place. This is an even exchange, since the bead on

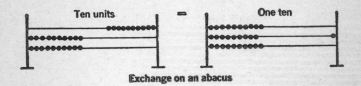

Exchange on an abacus

the second line stands for ten. Now we move two beads over on the top line, and the addition is complete. If we did this addition example with numerals written on paper, we would first add 5 and 7 to get 12. Then we would put down the 2 and carry 1 to the next column. The exchange of ten beads on the first line for one bead on the second line is equivalent to the *carry* step.

Although the abacus is only a toy in the United States, it is a practical calculator in the Soviet Union, China, Japan, and many other countries. The Japanese version of the abacus, called the *soroban,* is shown in the drawing below. A horizontal bar divides it into two parts. The beads below the bar represent, from right to left, units, tens, hun-

The number 162 on the Japanese soroban

dreds, etc. The beads above the bar represent five, fifty, five hundred, etc., respectively. Numbers are represented by moving the appropriate beads toward the bar from both sides. Experienced users of the soroban can calculate very quickly on it. Shortly after World War II, there was a calculating race between an American Army clerk, using an electrical desk calculator, and a Tokyo bank clerk using a soroban. The bank clerk won the race!

Two Types of Calculators

There are two major types of calculators in use today. They are distinguished by the manner in which they represent the numbers on which they perform calculations. One type is based on one of the ways in which we use numbers. The other type is based on the way we write numbers.

One of the important uses of numbers arises in the practical activity of measuring physical quantities. *Length* is an example of such a physical quantity. We measure a length by comparing it with a unit of length. The measure is then expressed as a number of units. In measurement, we use a number to represent a physical quantity. This process can be reversed. *We can use a physical quantity to represent a number.* Then, to perform arithmetic operations on numbers we can perform the corresponding operations on the physical quantities. This is what we were doing when we used two rulers as an adding machine. We represented each of the numbers by a length, and then we added the numbers by adding the lengths. Computers which represent numbers by physical quantities are called *analog computers.* The adding machine made of rulers is the simplest of analog computers. In other analog computers, numbers may be represented by such physical quantities as the amount of rotation of a wheel or the strength of an electric current.

When we write numbers in Arabic numerals, every number is represented by a sequence of digits. There are only ten digits in this system, 0, 1, 2, 3, 4, 5, 6, 7, 8, and 9. These ten symbols have no special qualifications for the job they do other than that they all look different. Any ten symbols that can be distinguished from each other can take their place. The symbols may be ink marks on paper, or sets of beads on a wire, or any physical object capable of appearing in ten distinct forms or of existing in ten distinct states. This opens up the possibility of using physical objects to represent digits. Then sequences of these physical objects can be used to represent numbers by representing their digits in the proper order. This is the underlying principle of the abacus. Each row of beads on the abacus can exist in ten states, viz., with no beads moved over, or with one bead moved over, or with two beads moved over, and so on. Each state represents a digit, and the sequence of rows of beads, each in a definite state, represents a number. Any computer that uses this principle is called a *digital computer*. The abacus is the simplest of digital computers. Since we move the beads of the abacus around by hand, it represents the lowest or hand-tool stage of evolution of digital computers. An electrical desk calculator is in the higher power-tool stage. The modern electronic calculators represent the most advanced or automatic-tool stage.

The Differential Analyzer

The best known of analog computers is the *differential analyzer* built at the Massachusetts Institute of Technology. In this machine, a number is represented as an amount of rotation of a wheel. Computations are made by combining the rotations of various wheels. There are two basic computing elements in the differential analyzer. One of them is a *differential gear*, like the gear assembly on the rear axle of an automobile. In the automobile the differential gear has the function of permitting the two rear wheels to turn at different speeds when the car makes a turn. In the differ-ential analyzer it has the job of computing the *average* of two numbers. The other computing unit is an *integrator*, which carries out mechanically one of the basic operations of the calculus. The analyzer makes computations by a sequence of steps in which it takes averages and performs integrations, just as the Turing machine makes calculations as a sequence of steps in which it writes or erases 1's and X's.

As an example of analog computation, we describe how a differential gear finds the average of two numbers. A differential gear is shown in the drawing below. It is an assembly of four gears, X, Y, Z, and W. Gears X and Y have the same number of teeth and are attached to sleeves on the axle of gear Z. Because of the sleeves, they can turn independently around the axle. Gear W is mounted on an axle across the cut-out section of gear Z. When gear Z turns, it carries gear W around with it. Gears X and Y are meshed with gear W as shown in the drawing. Suppose we want to average two numbers x and y. To represent x we turn gear X with a speed of x turns per second. To repre-

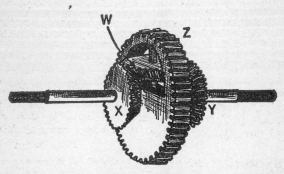

Differential Gear

sent y we turn gear Y with a speed of y turns per second in the same direction as gear X. Then the speed of gear Z will be $\dfrac{x+y}{2}$ turns per second. Let us see why.

Suppose first that x and y are equal numbers. Then gears X and Y turn with the same speed. In this case, gear W behaves like a rigid rod connecting gears X and Y. As gears X and Y turn, they push gear W, and in this way they make gear Z turn around with them at the same speed. However, if x and y are unequal numbers, so that gears X and Y turn at different speeds, then while gear W is being pushed it is also made to *turn* on its axle. Let us assume now that gear X is faster than gear Y, and let us denote by z the speed of gear Z. Imagine an observer who is on gear Z and turns with it. When he looks at gear X, he does not see all of its speed, because his own rotation with gear Z cancels part of it. He sees only the difference between the speed of gear X and the speed of gear Z. This difference is $x - z$. Similarly, when he observes gear Y, he sees only the difference between the speed of gear Y and the speed of gear Z. This difference is $z - y$. From his point of view, gear X passes him at the speed of $x - z$ and turns gear W as a result. Gear W then seems to be pushing gear Y, making it turn in a direction opposite to the turning of gear X. For every tooth on W that is pushed around by X, a tooth on the opposite side of W pushes Y. Therefore, as he sees it, the gears X and Y are turning at the same speed. That means that $x - z = z - y$. If we solve this simple equation for z, we find that $z = \dfrac{x+y}{2}$.

Once the differential gear has computed the average of two numbers, it is a simple matter to obtain their sum. If another gear with half as many teeth as gear Z is meshed directly with gear Z, it will turn twice as fast as gear Z does. So when the speed of gear Z is $\dfrac{x+y}{2}$, the speed of this smaller gear will be $x + y$. Note that this is the outcome only if gears X and Y are turning in the same direction. If we turn them in opposite directions, then the speed of gear Z will be $\dfrac{x-y}{2}$, and the speed of the smaller gear meshed with Z will be $x - y$. So a differential gear, with the help of just one more gear, can do addition and subtraction.

A Counting Machine

In a digital computer, a number is represented as a sequence of digits. If the numbers are expressed as Arabic numerals, the object which represents a single digit must be able to exist in ten distinct states, so that each state may stand for one of the digits from 0 to 9. An object that is frequently used for this purpose is a wheel whose circumference is divided into ten equal parts. The digits from 0 to 9 are printed on these parts in the proper order. Because of the circular arrangement, the 0 follows the 9. A viewing window near the wheel permits only one digit to be seen at a time. The ten "states" of the wheel are the ten positions to which the wheel may be turned so that different digits may be seen through the window. Several wheels like this, mounted side by side under one long window, can be used to display numbers with several digits. Combining the wheels with some gears can convert the set of wheels into a *counting machine*. One way of doing this is shown in the drawing. When the right hand wheel changes its state from 9 to 0, the cog over the gear on the left hand wheel pushes it and forces it to make one tenth of a turn. This makes the left hand wheel advance one step. That is, it changes its state, from whatever number it showed through the window to the next number on the wheel. The set of wheels is now equipped with a mechanism for *carrying*. In a hand-operated counting machine, a lever is pressed to register one unit. Every time the lever is pressed, the units wheel, which is on the far right, makes one tenth of a turn. If it starts with the 0 showing through the window, it advances one step at a time to 1, 2, 3, and so on, until it reaches 9. Then, the next time the lever is pressed, while the units wheel returns to 0, the tens wheel is advanced one step. In this way ten

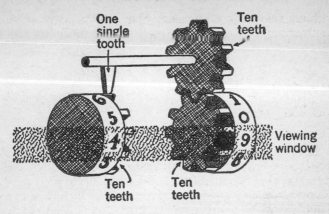

A counting machine

units on the units wheel are exchanged for a single ten on the tens wheel.

Counting devices of this type are frequently attached to machines that repeat the same operation over and over again. Then the device counts the number of times that the operation is performed. The *odometer* in an automobile is a counting machine used for counting the number of miles that the automobile travels. The first wheel of the odometer registers tenths of a mile. It is connected by means of a cable to a wheel of the car. When the wheel of the car has turned enough to move the car forward one tenth of a mile, the cable turns the first wheel of the odometer just enough to displace the digit that is under the viewing window, and move the next digit into place.

A Desk Calculator

To convert a counting machine into a hand-operated adding machine, all that is needed is an additional mechanical device for advancing each of the wheels by any chosen amount. In one type of adding machine, this device consists of a series of notched rods, one for each wheel of the counting machine. A row of buttons numbered from 0 to 9 is connected by levers to each rod. When a button is pressed down, the lever pushes the rod up until the number of teeth of the rod projecting beyond the wheel is equal to the number printed on the button. Then, when a hand lever is moved, the rod is pulled back. It engages the gear of the wheel as it moves, and advances it one step for each of the projecting teeth pulled back. In this way, the number on the button is added to the number previously registered on that wheel. Meanwhile, whenever the wheel completes a full turn, it *carries* one step over to the next wheel, so that the sum shows up as an Arabic numeral under the viewing window. When a sum has been completed, a lever is pressed to return all the wheels to the 0 state, so that the machine is ready to add a new set of numbers.

A machine that adds is easily adapted to do subtraction, multiplication, and division. Since it adds to the number on display through the viewing window by turning the wheels in one direction, it can subtract by turning the wheels in the opposite direction. It can multiply two numbers if it is equipped to register two numbers at a time. Then, as it keeps adding the multiplicand to itself on one register, it counts backwards from the multiplier to 1 on the other register. When it reaches 1, it has used the multiplicand as an addend a number of times equal to the multiplier. This is equivalent to multiplying by the multiplier. If it were set to multiply 4 × 5, for example, the pairs of numbers registered would be: 4, 5; 3, 10; 2, 15; 1, 20. When the multiplier has been reduced to 1, the number in the place of the multiplicand is the product. The machine can divide if it can be made to subtract a fixed number over and over again, and count the subtractions as it works. For example, to divide 35 by 11, the machine would start with 35 and keep subtracting 11, until the remainder is less than 11. If it displayed successive remainders and the count of the number of subtractions, the last count would be the quotient. In the division of 35 by 11, the successive pairs of numbers on display would be 24, 1; 13, 2; 2, 3. The final count of the subtractions is 3, so the quotient is 3.

One last modification is needed to speed up the process of calculation by the kind of machine we have been describing. The hand lever which is moved to carry out each step of addition or subtraction is replaced by an electric motor. When this is done, we have the basic elements of an electrical desk calculator. There are many such calculators available. They differ from each other in the details of mechanical design, but they all operate according to the same principles.

Change without Visible Motion

A great gain in speed of calculation is attained when moving parts such as levers and wheels are replaced by elements of an electrical circuit. Then the visible but slow motion of mechanical parts is replaced by the invisible but rapid motion of an electric current. The first step in designing a digital computer made of electrical elements would be to construct a device for representing digits, so that it can take over the job of the rotating wheel. If numbers are written as Arabic numerals, the device must be such that it can exist in any one of ten states. An example of such a device is a multiple switch that can route electric current into any one of ten separate lines. However, electrical elements, by their very nature, suggest a totally different approach to the problem of representing the digits of a number.

Switches, relays, and tubes are typical electrical elements. They have one simple and obvious characteristic in common. Each one of them may be either *on* or *off*. In other words each can exist in *two* states. This fact suggests that we use two states to represent digits, instead of straining to construct a device that has ten states. We need a ten-state device only when we write numbers as Arabic numerals. We can get by with a two-state device if we write numbers in the binary scale instead. The binary scale is the natural way of representing numbers by means of the state of electrical elements. That is why it is used in connection with electronic computers. The drawing below shows how a bank of four lamps can be used to represent the numbers from zero to nine. Each lamp represents one bit in the binary numeral for a number.

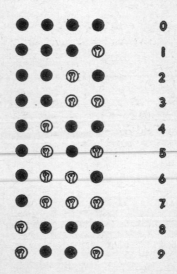

Numbers represented by lamps

Using binary numerals simplifies the problem of designing an electronic computer. But it also complicates the problem of using it. It compels us to translate numbers from the decimal scale to the binary scale before feeding them to the machine, and then translating the results of the machine's calculations back into the decimal scale. To avoid the extra steps of translation from one scale to another, some machines are designed on the basis of a compromise between the two scales. In these compromise machines, numbers are expressed by means of decimal digits, but each digit is written as four bits in the binary scale, as in the drawing on page 54. A two-digit number is expressed as two sets of four bits each. A three-digit number is expressed as three sets of four bits each, and so on. For example, if the word *OFF* is used to represent 0, and the word *ON* is used to represent 1, the decimal number 237 is represented by twelve bits as follows:

OFF OFF ON OFF   OFF OFF ON ON   OFF ON ON ON

This is so because OFF-OFF-ON-OFF represents the binary numeral 0010, which stands for *two;* OFF-OFF-ON-ON represents the binary numeral 0011, which stands for *three;* and OFF-ON-ON-ON represents the binary numeral 0111, which stands for *seven.*

In Chapter XI, where we describe some of the details of a typical electronic computer, we shall explain how numbers represented in this compromise form may be added or multiplied electrically.

CHAPTER 7

Words, Sentences, and Logic

Plain and Fancy Thinking

IN ORDER to design a machine that thinks, it is necessary to know the rules of thought. The study of the rules of thought is called *logic*. In this chapter we discover some of the principal ideas that occur in the study of logic. Then, in the next two chapters, we use these ideas to explore the rules of thought.

When you see the word "thinking," it may bring to your mind a picture of someone sitting in the pose of Rodin's statue of *The Thinker,* with his elbow on his knee and his chin on his hand, as he ponders the mysteries of the universe. Perhaps it suggests a lawyer threading his way through a complicated legal argument, or a mathematician writing out the proof of a theorem. In this age of specialization, we speak of some people as "thinkers" as if thinking were a specialized vocation engaged in only by a few. But no one has a monopoly on thinking. The plumber thinks when he decides how to cut and join pipes for a heating system. The housewife thinks when she plans a menu. A child thinks when he decides to climb a chair to reach a cookie on the table. The thinking of the philosopher, the lawyer and the mathematician is more intensive and more complicated than the common thinking of daily life, but it is built out of the same logical elements. All thinking, whether plain or fancy, follows the same rules.

Thoughts and Language

We express our thoughts in words. For this reason, the structure of thought is paralleled by the structure of language. We can get an idea of what is involved in thinking by examining the language we use. In fact, it will be enough to observe the language of a child as he learns to talk. Each stage in his language growth will introduce us to a major concept of logic.

Nouns and Classes

Let us accept without question the legend that the first word a baby learns is *Mama*. He soon learns his own name, say, *Peter*, and identifies *Daddy* and other members of the household. He also learns words like *spoon, cup, table*, and so on. Before long, he discovers that the words *Mama* and *table* are used in different ways. The word *Mama* is applied only to one object in his experience, the warm, gentle woman who feeds him, bathes him, dresses him, and hugs him. But the word *table* applies to several things. He may use it for the table in the kitchen, the table in the dining room, or the little table in his own bedroom. The word *table* is the name of a *class* of things, and is applied to any member of the class. Similarly, *spoon* and *cup* are class names, while *Peter* and *Daddy* refer to individuals only. In grammar, we distinguish between class names and the names of individuals by using different labels for them. We call a class name a *common noun*. We call an individual name a *proper noun*. To help us recognize the difference in writing, we capitalize proper nouns.

Underlying our use of common nouns, then, is the concept of a class. A class is any collection of objects that have some common property. The individual members of a class are referred to as *elements*. Any particular object may be an element of many classes. A dining room table, for example, may belong to the class of *wooden objects*. It also belongs to the class of *tables,* and to the class of *furniture.* Some classes overlap, or have common elements. The class of tables and the class of furniture have common elements. In fact, the class of tables lies wholly within the class of furniture. The class of furniture and the class of wooden objects also have common elements, but neither class lies wholly within the other. Not all wooden objects are articles of furniture, and not all pieces of furniture are made of wood. Some classes do not overlap at all. For example, the class of minerals and the class of animals have no common elements. No mineral is classified as an animal, and vice versa.

Sentences and Propositions

In a more advanced stage of a child's language growth, he begins to talk in whole sentences. Many of his sentences are statements or assertions. He may say, "The milk is hot," or "Peter is tired." He may seize his playmate's ball and say, "This ball is mine." An older child in a playful mood may string words together without rhyme or reason, to produce a sentence like, "The table sky jumps over the purple song." We observe immediately that we must distinguish between two kinds of sentences. Some sentences, like the first three, have a clear meaning. Other sentences, like the last one, have *no* meaning. The child sometimes makes up meaningless sentences to amuse himself or others. Lewis Carroll had the same purpose when he wrote:

> " 'Twas brillig, and the slithy toves
>   Did gyre and gimble in the wabe:
> All mimsy were the borograves,
>   And the mome raths outgrabe."

Unfortunately some people write meaningless sentences while they think they are communicating meaning to the reader. While we may, if we wish, think of a meaningless sentence as a form of music, it is not a means of expressing thought. In the study of logic, we have to consider only sentences with meaning.

A statement that has meaning is called a *proposition*. Every proposition is either true or false. The truth or falsity of a proposition is called its *truth value*.

Propositional Forms

The statement, "The last note on the right on a piano keyboard has a higher pitch than middle C," is a proposition. If we replace the first ten words (the complete subject of the sentence) by a blank space, we obtain what is called a *propositional form:* "——————— has a higher pitch than middle C." The propositional form is not a proposition. It is not even a sentence. It becomes a sentence, however, if we fill the blank space with some subject. Here, for example, are three sentences obtained by filling in the blank space with different subjects:

1) The second note from the right on a piano keyboard has a higher pitch than middle C.
2) The last note on the left on a piano keyboard has a higher pitch than middle C.
3) My hat has a higher pitch than middle C.

Notice that while all three are sentences, they aren't all propositions. Sentences 1 and 2 have meaning. The first one is true, and the second one is false. These are both propositions. But sentence 3 has no meaning. Therefore it is not a proposition. If we want to obtain a proposition from a propositional form, we are not free to fill the blank space with any subject at all. We must choose only subjects which yield a sentence that makes sense (whether it is true or false). A set of subjects that makes sense when put into a propositional form is called a *universe of discourse*. In this case, for example, we might choose as the universe of discourse the set of all notes on a piano keyboard.

A blank space is easy to show in writing, but hardly easy to express out loud. To be able to speak a propositional form as well as to write it, we take a cue from elementary algebra, and use a variable to serve as a place holder. If we use the variable X, then the propositional form is written in this way: X has a higher pitch than middle C. If X is replaced by any element in the universe of discourse, a meaningful sentence or proposition is obtained. For some of these elements, the proposition is true. The set of all such elements for which the proposition is true is a class within the universe of discourse. The propositional form, "X has a higher pitch than middle C," is called the *defining form* of that class.

Every class can be defined by means of a defining form. The procedure for defining a class is to specify first some universe of discourse within which the class may be found. Then set up a defining form which becomes a true proposition for elements of the universe of discourse that are in the class, and which becomes a false proposition for elements of the universe of discourse that are not in the class. The defining form serves as a kind of filter, sifting members of the class out of the universe of discourse. For example, to define a square, we might choose as the universe of discourse the set of all rectangles, and then use as the defining form, "X has equal sides."

Once a universe of discourse is specified, every class within it can be defined by means of an appropriate defining form. The procedure is also clearly reversible. Every defining form which makes sense in that universe of discourse defines a class within it. This fact shows that there is a close connection between the concept of *class* and the concept of *proposition*. It should not come as a surprise, then, to find that there is a close connection between the algebra of classes, which will be developed in Chapter VIII, and the algebra of propositions, which will be developed in Chapter IX.

Relations

Some of the words that a child learns very early denote *relations* between things. When he says, "The cup is on the table," the word *on* specifies a relation between the cup and the table. When he says, "Mr. Green is Johnny's daddy," he uses the word daddy (note the small d) to denote the relation "father of." In his early experiences with numbers, he learns of the relation "smaller than" that exists between certain numbers.

One of the problems that comes up in logic is to discover the properties possessed by relations, and to classify the relations according to their properties. Let us consider, for example, the relation *smaller than*. It is customary to represent it by the symbol $<$. Then the statement, "Two is smaller than three," can be written this way: $2 < 3$. It is a well-known fact about the *smaller than* relation that it has this property: If the first of three numbers is smaller than the second, and the second is smaller than the third, then the first is smaller than the third. This property is called the *transitive* property, because the *smaller than* relation passes right through the middle number to connect the first and third number. (*Transit* means goes through.)

Not all relations have the transitive property. For example, the relation *father of* does not have the transitive property. If John is the father of Fred, and Fred is the father of Henry, it is not true that John is the father of Henry.

Relations among Classes or Propositions

There are certain special relations that classes within a universe of discourse may have to each other. We have already encountered some of them. For example, two classes may have some elements in common. If they do, we shall say that they *intersect*. A particularly important case of intersection arises when one class lies wholly within another. For convenience, let us now use variables A, B, and C to denote classes within a certain universe of discourse. If A lies wholly within B, we shall say that A is a subclass of B. To denote the relation "is a subclass of" we shall use the symbol $\subset$. (Read $\subset$ as "is a subclass of" or "is included in.") Then the statement, *"A is a subclass of B,"* can be written in this form: $A \subset B$. It is easy to see that if A is a subclass of B, and B is a subclass of C, then A is a subclass of C. Consequently, the relation $\subset$, like the relation $<$, has the transitive property. In fact the symbol for "is a subclass of" was deliberately made to resemble the symbol for "is smaller than" in order to remind us that the two relations have similar properties.

There are certain special relations that hold between some propositions. A particularly important one is the relation of *implication*. For example, the proposition, "It is raining," implies the proposition, "The street is wet." (That is, if the first proposition is true, the second one must also be true.) "The street is wet" implies that "Anyone walking on the street will get his shoes wet." From these two implications we obtain another one: "It is raining" implies that "Anyone walking on the street will get his shoes wet." We obtained this third implication by using the following well-known rule of logic: If one proposition implies a second proposition, and the second proposition implies a third proposition, then the first proposition implies the third proposition. In other words, the relation "implies" has the transitive property. To show it in abbreviated form, we shall use the symbol $\rightarrow$ for the relation "implies," and we shall use the letters p, q, and r as variables that may stand for propositions. Then we can state that the relation $\rightarrow$ is transitive in this way: If $p \rightarrow q$, and $q \rightarrow r$, then $p \rightarrow r$.

In the next two chapters we explore more relations among classes, and relations among propositions. We have already seen that the relation $\subset$, which connects some classes, and the relation $\rightarrow$, which connects some propositions, resembles the relation $<$, which connects some numbers. We shall find more such resemblances between the

behavior of classes or propositions to the behavior of numbers. In fact, there will be enough resemblances to permit
us to develop an algebra of classes and an algebra of
propositions.

CHAPTER 8

Algebra of Classes

Classes in a Universe

PICK any collection of objects whatever as a universe of discourse. We shall call this collection the universe class, or, more briefly, the *universe*. By selecting elements within this universe in different ways, we can form classes that are included within the universe. They will all be subclasses of the universe class. The purpose of this chapter is to examine relationships among the set of all possible subclasses of the universe class.

We might, for example, choose as the universe class the set of all living people. We can define a variety of subclasses within this universe by means of defining forms. Here are some examples:

1. X is a resident of the United States.
2. X is a citizen of the United States.
3. X is a resident of New York City.
4. X is the author of this book.
5. X is President of the United States.
6. X is a living person.
7. X is dead.

The class specified by each defining form is the class of all those living persons for whom the defining form becomes a true statement when X is replaced by a member of the class. Notice that the classes defined by 1, 2, and 3 include some but not all members of the universe class. The class defined by 6, on the other hand, includes all members of the universe class. That is, the universe class is one of its own subclasses. The classes defined by 4 and 5 contain exactly one member each. A class that contains one and only one member is called a *unit class*. The class defined by 7 contains no members at all. We call it the *empty class*. We shall have to refer to the universe class and the empty class quite often, so we introduce special symbols for them. We shall use the symbol 1 to stand for the universe class, and the symbol 0 to stand for the empty class. The reason for this choice of symbols will soon be apparent.

A Small Universe

The relationships within a universe class are especially easy to see if the universe class contains only a few members. As an example, let us take as the universe class the set of three symbols, #, %, and $. We shall form all possible subclasses of this universe class. To specify a class, we shall put its members on display between a pair of braces, { }. For convenience in referring to these classes, we shall give each one a name. The universe class and the empty class already have names, 1 and 0. To name the other classes, we shall use capital letters such as A, B, and C, chosen from the beginning of the alphabet. For variables that may stand for any class we shall use capital letters, such as X, Y, and Z, chosen from the end of the alphabet. Here is a complete list of all the subclasses within this small universe, together with their names:

$$
\begin{aligned}
\text{The universe} \quad &= 1 = \{\#, \%, \$\} \\
A &= \{\#, \%\} \\
B &= \{\#, \$\} \\
C &= \{\%, \$\} \\
D &= \{\#\} \\
E &= \{\%\} \\
F &= \{\$\} \\
\text{The empty class} = 0 &= \{\ \}
\end{aligned}
$$

To form a subclass of any of the classes in this list, simply delete all, or some, or none of its members. If we begin with the class B, for example, and omit no elements we are left with $\{\#, \$\}$ or B. If we omit \$, we are left with $\{\#\}$ or D. If we omit $\#$, we are left with $\{\$\}$ or F. If we omit both \$ and $\#$, we are left with $\{\ \}$ or 0. So the subclasses of B are B, D, F, and 0. Then using the symbol $\subset$ for the relation "is a subclass of," we may say $B \subset B$, $D \subset B$, $F \subset B$, and $0 \subset B$. The subclasses of C are C, E, F, and 0. So we may say $C \subset C$, $E \subset C$, $F \subset C$, and $0 \subset C$.

The Subclass Relation

By using this small universe as a model, we can verify a few simple rules about the symbol $\subset$. It is not hard to see that these rules are true in any universe whatever:

The empty class is a subclass of every class in the universe. In symbols, the rule takes this form: $0 \subset X$, where X is a variable that may stand for any subclass of the universe class.

Since the only classes we are talking about are subclasses of the universe class, we may say that every class is a subclass of the universe. In symbols: $X \subset 1$.

Every class is a subclass of itself. In symbols: $X \subset X$.

We have already observed that the relation $\subset$ has the transitive property. In symbols: If $X \subset Y$, and $Y \subset Z$, then $X \subset Z$.

We shall call two classes equal if they have the same membership. From time to time, we shall have to compare two classes to see if they are equal. A simple test for equality of classes is provided by this rule: Two classes are equal if each of them is a subclass of the other. In symbols: If $X \subset Y$, and $Y \subset X$, then $X = Y$.

There are at least two classes in the universe that are not equal. For example, the universe class is not equal to the empty class, because the empty class contains no members, while the universe class does contain members. (This rule breaks down only in the exceptional case where the universe class is the empty class. But in this case, with an empty universe of discourse, we have nothing to talk about. So let us agree now not to consider this exceptional case at all.) In symbols, the rule takes this form: there is a class X and a class Y such that $X \neq Y$. (Read $\neq$ as "is *not* equal to.")

Venn Diagrams

We shall find it helpful in the rest of this chapter to draw diagrams to illustrate the relationships between classes. The special diagrams we use are called Venn diagrams, after John Venn, a British mathematician of the nineteenth century. In the Venn diagrams, the universe is represented by the points inside a rectangle. A subclass of the universe is represented by the points inside some area within the rectangle. The area used most often to represent a subclass is a circle. The first diagram below shows a subclass A within the universe. The second diagram shows another subclass B lying wholly within A. This illustrates the relationship $B \subset A$.

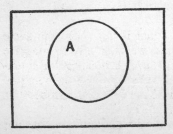
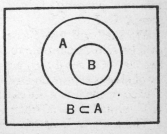

$B \subset A$

New Classes from Old

We now introduce some operations by which we can combine two classes to form a third class in the same universe. To make the meaning of each operation clear, we shall draw an appropriate Venn diagram that illustrates it. We shall also apply the operations in our model universe of three elements, #, %, and $.

The first operation we define is *addition* of classes, and it will be represented by means of a plus sign. If X and Y are classes in the universe 1, then $X + Y$ is the class made up of all those elements in the universe that are in X or in Y. (In logic this class is understood to include elements that are in both classes.) Note that the most significant idea here is expressed by the word *or*. In the Venn diagram below, if X is represented by the circle with vertical shading, and Y is represented by the circle with horizontal shading, then $X + Y$ is represented by the total shaded area enclosed within the thick black line.

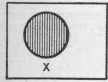 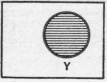 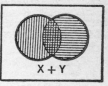

Addition of classes

In the universe $1 = \{ \#, \%, \$ \}$ (see page 65)
$B = \{ \#, \$ \}$, and $C = \{ \%, \$ \}$, So
$B + C = \{ \#, \%, \$ \}$. That is, $B + C = 1$.
$D = \{ \# \}$, and $E = \{ \% \}$. So $D + E = \{ \#, \% \} = A$.
$E = \{ \% \}$ and $F = \{ \$ \}$. So $E + F = \{ \%, \$ \} = C$.

If X and Y are classes in the same universe, $X + Y$ is called their *sum*. It is also sometimes called their *union*, because it is obtained by uniting within one class all the elements that are found in the two classes. The system of subclasses of a universe is closed under the operation +, because if X and Y are subclasses of the universe, so is $X + Y$.

Rules about Addition

Some simple rules governing the addition of classes follow immediately from the definition:

Uniting the elements of X and Y yields the same result as uniting the elements of Y and X. In symbols: $X + Y = Y + X$. (Commutative Law of Addition.) For example, if $B = \{\#, \$\}$ and $C = \{\%, \$\}$, $B + C$ contains all the elements of B, as well as the element $\%$ which is in C but not in B. $C + B$ contains all the elements of C, as well as the element $\#$ which is in B but not in C. In both cases, the total membership contains exactly the same elements, $\#$, $\%$, and $\$$. So $B + C = C + B$.

If X, Y and Z are classes, uniting X with the sum of Y and Z yields the same result as uniting the sum of X and Y with Z. In symbols: $X + (Y + Z) = (X + Y) + Z$. (Associative Law of Addition.) This rule is illustrated by the Venn diagrams below:

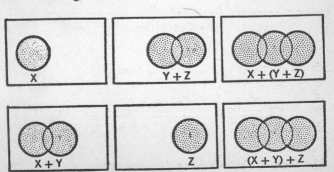

The associative law of addition

If any class is united with itself, the result is the same class all over again, because it includes all the elements of the original class, and no new elements. In symbols: $X + X = X$.

A class is unchanged if you unite it with the empty class, since the empty class contributes no additional elements. In symbols: $X + 0 = X$. (Law of 0.)

If any class is united with the universe, the result is the universe. This is clearly true because the union of any class with the universe must contain all elements in the universe, and cannot contain any others. In symbols: $X + 1 = 1$.

A class is wholly included in any union it forms with another class. In symbols: $X \subset X + Y$.

Notice that some of the rules governing addition of classes are like rules governing addition of numbers: the Commutative Law, the Associative Law, and the Law of 0. However, some of the rules for addition of classes like $X + X = X$, and $X + 1 = 1$, have no counterpart in the addition of numbers.

Multiplication of Classes

The second operation we define is *multiplication* of classes. As in the algebra of numbers, we shall represent multiplication by means of a dot, but this dot will often be omitted. If X and Y are classes in the universe 1, then XY is the class made up of all those elements that are in both X *and* Y. Note that the most significant idea here is

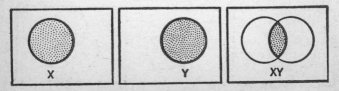

Multiplication of classes

expressed by the word *and*, The result of multiplying two classes is called their *product,* or their *intersection.* The Venn diagram for a product is shown on page 70.

In the universe $1 = \{\#, \%, \$\}$, $BC = \{\$\} = F$. There are no elements that belong to both D and E, so $DE = 0$.

The system of subclasses of a universe is closed under multiplication, because if X and Y are subclasses of the universe, then so is XY.

Rules about Multiplication

These rules governing multiplication of classes are easily verified:

The set of elements in both X and Y is the same as the set of elements in both Y and X. In symbols: $XY = YX$. (Commutative Law of Multiplication.)

If X, Y and Z are classes, multiplying X by the product of Y and Z yields the same result as multiplying the product of X and Y by Z. In symbols: $X(YZ) = (XY)Z$. (Associative Law of Multiplication.) This rule is illustrated by the Venn diagrams below.

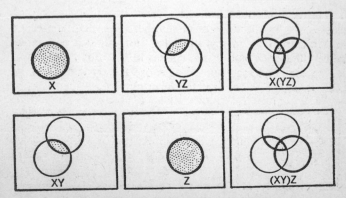

The associative law of multiplication

If X is any class, there are no elements that are in both the empty class and in X. Therefore multiplying any class by the empty class yields the empty class as the product. In symbols: $0X = 0$.

If X is any class, the elements that belong to the universe and to X are precisely the elements of X. So multiplying the universe by any class yields that same class as the product. In symbols: $1X = X$. (Law of 1.)

If any class is multiplied by itself, the same class is the product, because the elements in both X and X are obviously merely the elements in X. In symbols: $XX = X$.

If two classes X and Y are multiplied, the product is a subclass of either class. This is immediately obvious from the Venn diagram. In symbols: $XY \subset X$, and $XY \subset Y$.

Among these rules governing the multiplication of classes, there are some like the rules governing the multiplication of numbers: the Commutative Law, the Associative Law, and the Law of 1. However, there are also some rules, like $XX = X$, that do not apply to numbers at all.

The Distributive Laws

In the algebra of numbers, we had the distributive law: $X(Y + Z) = XY + XZ$. We can verify by means of Venn diagrams that this law holds for classes, too. The expression $X(Y + Z)$ means first unite Y and Z to form $Y + Z$, and then find the class of elements common to X and $Y + Z$. The expression $XY + XZ$ means first multiply X by Y and multiply X by Z. Then unite the two products. The two procedures are shown in these Venn diagrams below.

Comparing the two end results, we see that they are the same.

The law that $X(Y + Z) = XY + XZ$ may be put into

words as follows: To multiply a sum of two classes by a third class, it is just as good to multiply each of the two classes separately by that third class, and then add the products. It is interesting to see what becomes of this law if

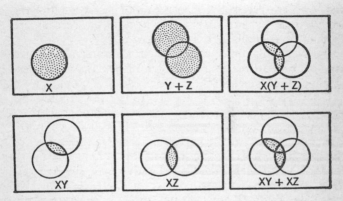

Multiplication is distributive with respect to addition

we interchange the words add and multiply, and interchange the words sum and product. Then, with a slight adjustment of language to conform to our customary word order, we get this statement: To add a third class to the product of two classes, it is just as good to add it to each of the two classes first, and then multiply the sums. In symbols, this statement says that $X + (YZ) = (X + Y) (X + Z)$. The original law says that multiplication is distributive with respect to addition. The new statement says that addition is distributive with respect to multiplication. The original law is true for both natural numbers and classes. Is the new statement also a law for natural numbers and classes?

To see if the new statement applies to numbers, let $X = 2$, $Y = 3$, and $Z = 4$. Then the statement says that $2 + (3 \cdot 4) = (2 + 3) (2 + 4)$, or $2 + 12 = 5 \cdot 6$. This assertion is obviously not true, so the new statement is *not* a law for natural numbers. However, it *is* a law for classes, as you can see from the Venn diagrams. So for classes, we have two distributive laws: Multiplication is distributive with respect to addition, and addition is distributive with respect to multiplication.

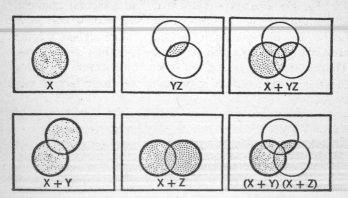

Addition is distributive with respect to multiplication

The Complement

We introduce a third operation of classes called *taking the complement*. If X is a class in the universe, the complement of X is the class obtained when you remove from the universe all the members of X. The operation of taking the complement is denoted by a bar drawn over the name of a class. Thus, the complement of X is written as $\bar{X}$. The operation is illustrated by the Venn diagram below.

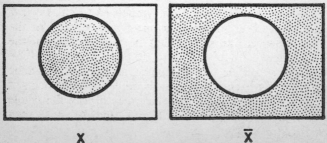

As an example of taking the complement, let us find the complement of B in the universe $1 = \{ \#, \%, \$ \}$. $B = \{ \#, \$ \}$. Therefore $\bar{B} = \{ \% \} = E$. For a second example, let the universe be the class of all living people, and let X be the class of residents of the United States. Then $\bar{X}$ is the class of living people who do *not* reside in the United States. The bar denoting taking the complement serves the same function as the word *not* in ordinary speech. In fact, $\bar{X}$ may be read as "not X."

In any universe, it is obvious that the complement of the universe is the empty class and vice versa.

Rules about Complements

These rules follow directly from the definition of complement:

If you unite any class with its complement, you are putting into one class all the elements *in* the original class and all the elements *not in* the original class. The result obviously includes the whole universe. In symbols: $X + \bar{X} = 1$.

There are no elements that are in a class and also not in that class. So the product of a class and its complement is the empty class. In symbols: $X\bar{X} = 0$.

Since a class and its complement divide the universe between them, without any overlapping, then each is the complement of the other. Hence the complement of the complement of X is X itself. In symbols $(\bar{\bar{X}}) = X$. For example, saying that someone is *not* a *non*-resident of the United States is like saying that he *is* a resident of the United States.

There is a simple test by which complements can be recognized. Two classes are each other's complements if they do not overlap, and, together, they fill out the whole universe. In symbols: If $X + Y = 1$, and $XY = 0$, then $X = \bar{Y}$ and $Y = \bar{X}$.

Sums Versus Products

The fact that every class in a universe has a complement in that universe leads to an interesting pair of laws known as the laws of duality. These laws say that the complement of the sum of two classes is the product of their complements, and that the complement of the product of two

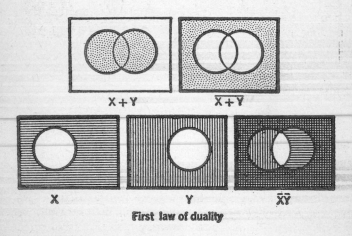

First law of duality

classes is the sum of their complements. In symbols: $(\overline{X + Y}) = \overline{X}\overline{Y}$, and $(\overline{XY}) = \overline{X} + \overline{Y}$.

The first of these laws is verified in the Venn diagrams above. In the first line of diagrams, we first add X and Y, and then take the complement of the sum. In the second line of diagrams, we first take the complement of X and Y and then multiply these complements. $\overline{X}$ is shown by horizontal shading. $\overline{Y}$ is shown by vertical shading. If the two diagrams are superposed, the product $\overline{X} \cdot \overline{Y}$ is the area that has both horizontal and vertical shading. Inspection of the last diagram on each line shows that the results are equal.

Venn diagrams can be used in the same way to verify the second law of duality.

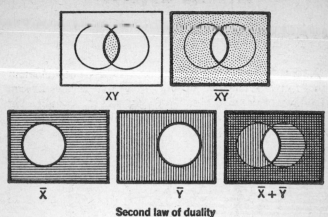

Second law of duality

Subclass Redefined

We have introduced a special symbol ⊂ for the concept "is a subclass of." However, we can do without this symbol, because the same concept can be expressed by means of a sum or a product of classes. The Venn diagram below shows the situation when X is a subclass of Y. It is clear in this situation that the part of X and Y that is common to both is precisely X. So, if $X ⊂ Y$, then $XY = X$. On the other hand, if $XY = X$, it means that

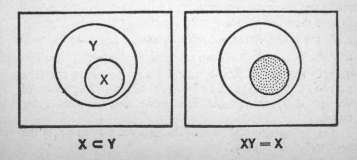

$X ⊂ Y$ $XY = X$

X is the common part of X and Y, so that X is wholly included in Y, or $X \subset Y$. Hence the statement $X \subset Y$ is completely equivalent to the statement $XY = X$, and either statement may be replaced by the other. It is easily seen that the statement $X \subset Y$ is also equivalent to the statement $X + Y = Y$. If X lies wholly within Y, uniting X and Y does not enlarge the class Y at all. So the union of X and Y in this case is precisely Y. Conversely, if the union of X and Y is precisely Y, it means that X has contributed to the union only elements that are in Y, hence X lies wholly within Y.

Some Rules Imply Others

The rules about classes that we have observed so far are not entirely independent of each other. Some of them can be derived from others. This fact suggests that the algebra of classes be organized into a deductive system analogous to that of geometry. In high school geometry we are taught many rules about geometric figures. But they are not presented as isolated facts. They are organized into a system in this way: A small set of rules, known as *axioms*, is separated from the rest in order to serve as the foundation of the system. Then all the other rules are derived from the axioms by logical reasoning. The derived rules are known as *theorems*. No verbal definitions are given of the terms used in the axioms. The meaning of these terms consists solely of what the axioms say about them. For example, we do not try to define the words *point* and *line* in geometry. But we know from the axioms that there is one and only one line through any two points. This assertion is part of the meaning of the words *point* and *line*. However, when new terms, not already mentioned in the axioms, are introduced in the system, they are carefully defined first.

We can follow the same procedure with the rules of the

algebra of classes. We can select from these rules a core set of rules that may serve as axioms, from which we can derive all the other rules as theorems. There are many different ways of selecting the rules that will serve as axioms. One particular choice of the axioms is given below.

Axioms for the Algebra of Classes

Here is a set of axioms for the algebra of classes. The undefined terms used in these axioms are "class," "plus" and "times." The usual symbols are used to represent "plus" and "times."

I. If X and Y are classes, there is a class Z such that $X + Y = Z$.

II. If X and Y are classes, there is a class W such that $XY = W$.

III. There exists a class 0 such that, if X is any class, $X + 0 = X$.

IV. There exists a class 1 such that, if X is any class, $1X = X$.

V. If X and Y are classes, $X + Y = Y + X$.

VI. If X and Y are classes, $XY = YX$.

VII. If X, Y and Z are classes, $X + YZ = (X + Y)(X + Z)$.

VIII. If X, Y and Z are classes, $X(Y + Z) = XY + XZ$.

IX. If X is a class, there exists a class $\bar{X}$ such that $X + \bar{X} = 1$, and $X\bar{X} = 0$.

X. There exist classes X and Y such that $X \neq Y$.

Axioms I and II merely assert that any two classes have a sum and a product. Axioms III and IV are the Law of 0 and the Law of 1, respectively. Axioms V and VI are the commutative laws of addition and multiplication. Axioms VII and VIII are the two distributive laws. Axiom IX asserts that every class has a complement. Axiom X guarantees that the system includes classes that are not empty.

Notice that the associative laws for addition and multiplication are not included among the axioms. They can be derived as theorems from these ten axioms. Notice, too, that the concept of *subclass* is not included among the undefined terms. We can, if we wish, define this concept by using the terms that do appear in the axioms. For example, we might introduce the following definition: $X \subset Y$ shall mean that $XY = X$.

One of the very important rules of logic is the rule that the relation $\subset$ is transitive. That is, if $X \subset Y$, and $Y \subset Z$, then $X \subset Z$. This rule is not an axiom, so it must be a theorem. That is, we should be able to *prove* it with the help of the axioms and other theorems. The proof turns out to be quite simple: If $X \subset Y$, and $Y \subset Z$, then by the definition of $\subset$, $XY = X$, and $XZ = Y$. The latter statement means that Y can be replaced by YZ. Making this substitution in the statement $XY = X$, we get $X(YZ) = X$. The associative law of multiplication says that we may replace $X(YZ)$ by $(XY)Z$. Making this substitution, we get the statement that $(XY)Z = X$. But, since $XY = X$, we may replace XY by X. The resulting statement, $XZ = X$, is equivalent to the statement that $X \subset Z$.

Axiom IX asserts that every class has a complement. It seems to leave open the possibility that a class may have more than one complement. However, all the axioms taken together exclude this possibility. It can be proved as a theorem that every class has only one complement having the properties listed in Axiom IX. Consequently, any time we come across two classes X and Y such that $X + Y = 1$, and $XY = 0$, we can conclude at once that $X = \bar{Y}$ and $Y = \bar{X}$. (That is, each is the complement of the other.)

All of the rules that we have listed about addition and multiplication of classes that are not in the list of axioms are theorems that can be proved. In what follows we shall assume that they have been proved.

Abstract Boolean Algebra

We obtained the rules which we have called Axioms I to X by first taking some fixed universe class, and then observing relationships among the subclasses of that universe class. Our daily experience with classes and subclasses is the mother which has given birth to these axioms. But now, like any live child, this set of axioms begins to lead an independent existence. We cut the umbilical cord which ties the axioms to their mother by forgetting that the axioms refer to subclasses of a universe class. We think of them as referring to some collection of objects whose properties, as far as we are interested in them, are only those asserted by the axioms, and by theorems that can be derived from the axioms. The infant system, thus given independent status, is called Abstract Boolean Algebra, a branch of pure mathematics named after the British logician George Boole, who was the first to construct an algebra of logic. To make the separation from the concept of class absolutely clear, we replace the word class wherever it appears in Axioms I to X by the expression, "element of the system."

When we separate the axioms from the class concept from which we derived them in the first place, it may look as though we are robbing them of their content. Actually, we are enriching them, and giving ourselves a tool of greater power.

There are *many different systems* for which the axioms of Boolean Algebra are true statements. So far we have become acquainted only with systems that consist of subclasses of a universe class. In later chapters, we shall be introduced to some others. By disregarding for the time being any specific interpretations of Boolean Algebra, and developing it in abstract form, we guarantee that the theorems that we derive apply to *all* systems which satisfy the axioms. Thus, the theorems we derive will apply to the algebra of classes of this chapter. But they will also apply to the algebra of propositions of the next chapter, and to the algebra of switching circuits described in Chapter X.

Examples of Boolean Algebras

The set of all subclasses of some universe class is a Boolean algebra. By choosing universe classes of different sizes, we can get examples of many different Boolean algebras. For example, if the universe class is the set of three elements #, %, and $, then it has eight subclasses, 1, *A, B, C, D, E, F,* and 0, as defined on page 65. These eight elements, related to each other by the operations of addition, multiplication, and taking the complement, constitute a Boolean algebra. The relationships within this system can be given explicitly in the form of tables as follows:

Addition Table									Multiplication Table									Table of Complements	
+	1	A	B	C	D	E	F	0	·	1	A	B	C	D	E	F	0	X	X̄
1	1	1	1	1	1	1	1	1	1	1	A	B	C	D	E	F	0	1	0
A	1	A	1	1	A	A	1	A	A	A	A	D	E	D	E	0	0	A	F
B	1	1	B	1	B	1	B	B	B	B	D	B	F	D	0	F	0	B	E
C	1	1	1	C	1	C	C	C	C	C	E	F	C	0	E	F	0	C	D
D	1	A	B	1	D	A	B	D	D	D	D	D	0	D	0	0	0	D	C
E	1	A	1	C	A	E	C	E	E	E	E	0	E	0	E	0	0	E	B
F	1	1	B	C	B	C	F	F	F	F	0	F	F	0	0	F	0	F	A
0	1	A	B	C	D	E	F	0	0	0	0	0	0	0	0	0	0	0	1

If the universe class is the set of two symbols, @ and ¢, then it has these subclasses:

$$1 = \{ @, ¢ \} \quad A = \{ @ \} \quad B = \{ ¢ \} \quad 0 = \{ \quad \}$$

These four elements constitute a Boolean algebra whose internal relationships are expressed in these tables:

Addition Table +	1	A	B	0
1	1	1	1	1
A	1	A	1	A
B	1	1	B	B
0	1	A	B	0

Multiplication Table ·	1	A	B	0
1	1	A	B	0
A	A	A	0	0
B	B	0	B	0
0	0	0	0	0

Table of Complements X	$\bar{X}$
1	0
A	B
B	A
0	1

If the universe class is a unit class (containing only one member) then it has only two subclasses, 1 and 0, the universe class and the empty class. These two elements together constitute a Boolean algebra whose complete structure is revealed in these tables:

Addition Table +	1	0
1	1	1.
0	1	0

Multiplication Table ·	1	0
1	1	0
0	0	0

Table of Complements X	$\bar{X}$
1	0
0	1

The Boolean algebra with only two elements is called a two-valued algebra. It is the simplest possible example of a Boolean algebra. It is also a very important one, as we shall see in the next chapter.

Some Theorems Proved

Proving a theorem in Boolean algebra is a purely mathematical exercise. To show what some further theorems are like, and to demonstrate the techniques of proof, we shall now carry out a few proofs in detail.

First we prove that if X and Y are elements of a Boolean algebra, then $X (X + Y) = X$. We prove it by building up a sequence of expressions in which $X (X + Y)$ is the first expression and X is the last expression. We show at the same time that each expression is equal to the one that follows it in the sequence. Each equality is justified by an axiom or theorem that we know already. The chain of equalities will assure us that the first expression, $X(X + Y)$, is equal to the last expression, X, in the sequence:

$$X(X + Y) = (X + 0) (X + Y),$$ since by axiom, I, X can be replaced by $X + 0$,

$$= X + (0 \cdot Y)$$, by axiom XII,

$$= X + 0$$, since $0 \cdot Y = 0$,

$$= X$$, by axiom III.

As an example of the meaning of this theorem, let us apply it to the case where X is the class of people who have blue eyes, and Y is the class of people who have hair on their heads. Then reading the multiplication sign as *and,* and the plus sign as *or,* we find that the theorem makes this assertion: The class of people who have blue eyes and who either have blue eyes or have hair on their heads is identical with the class of people who have blue eyes.

In a similar manner, we prove that $X + XY = X$:

$$X + XY = 1 \cdot X + XY$$ by axiom IV,

$$= X \cdot 1 + XY$$ by axiom VI,

$$= X (1 + Y)$$ by axiom VIII,

$$= X \cdot 1$$ since $1 + Y = 1$,

$$= 1 \cdot X$$ by axiom VI,

$$= X$$ by axiom IV.

From this theorem we get the assertion that the class of people who either have blue eyes or have blue eyes and also have hair on their heads is identical with the class of people who have blue eyes.

A third theorem that is easily proved asserts that $XY + X\overline{Y} = X$:

$$
\begin{aligned}
XY + X\overline{Y} &= X(Y + \overline{Y}) && \text{by axiom VIII,} \\
&= X \cdot 1 && \text{by axiom IX,} \\
&= 1 \cdot X && \text{by axiom VI,} \\
&= X && \text{by axiom IV.}
\end{aligned}
$$

If 1 is the class of all people, and Y is the class of all people who have hair on their heads, then $\overline{Y}$ is the class of all bald people. Then the third theorem asserts that the class of people who either have blue eyes and have hair on their heads or have blue eyes and are bald is the same as the class of people who have blue eyes.

As a fourth example, we prove that $(X + Y)(X + \overline{Y}) = X$:

$$
\begin{aligned}
(X + Y)(X + \overline{Y}) &= X + (Y\overline{Y}) && \text{by axiom VII,} \\
&= X + 0 && \text{by axiom IX,} \\
&= X && \text{by axiom III.}
\end{aligned}
$$

Interpreting X and Y in the same way as we have above, we learn from this theorem that the class of people of whom it is true that they either have blue eyes or have hair on their heads while it is also true that they either have blue eyes or are bald is identical with the class of people who have blue eyes.

Equivalent Expressions

Each of the theorems just proved asserts that two expressions are equivalent. One of the expressions is complicated, while the other one is simple. In the last theorem, for instance, we assert that the complicated expression, $(X + Y)(X + \bar{Y})$, is equivalent to the simple expression, X. This is a good thing to know, because it entitles us to replace the complicated expression by the simpler one. If X and Y are classes, as in the interpretation we used four times above, then the theorem permits us to replace a complicated description of a class by a much shorter and simpler description of the same class. Sometimes a clause in a contract is a complicated description of a class of circumstances. If the clause is expressed symbolically, it is often possible to simplify the clause by means of Boolean algebra.

In Chapter X we shall deal with situations in which the variables used in Boolean algebra stand for switches. Then the theorems such as those we have proved give us ways of simplifying a complicated switching circuit. When Boolean algebra is used for this purpose it pays dividends in money saved through economy of design.

The Law of Duality

To underscore the practical importance of Boolean algebra as a means of simplifying circuit designs, we now prove algebraically some theorems that we shall use in Chapter XI, when we discuss the design of electronic computers. The first of these theorems is the law of duality. The other two are consequences of this law.

We shall prove the law of duality that asserts that $\overline{(X + Y)} = \bar{X}\bar{Y}$. Expressed in words, this law says that $\bar{X}\bar{Y}$ is the complement of $X + Y$. To prove that this statement is true, all we need do is show that the sum of $X + Y$ and $\bar{X}\bar{Y}$ is 1, while their product is 0. (See page 75.)

To show that the sum of $X + Y$ and $\bar{X}\bar{Y}$ is 1, we begin with the true statement, $X + \bar{X} = 1$. Since we have proved that $X + XY = X$, we can replace X by $X + XY$. Since $\bar{X} = 1 \cdot \bar{X} = \bar{X} \cdot 1$, we can replace $\bar{X}$ by $\bar{X} \cdot 1$. Then we have: $(X + XY) + \bar{X} \cdot 1 = 1$. Since $Y + \bar{Y} = 1$, we may replace the 1 on the left hand side of the equation by $Y + \bar{Y}$. Now we have: $(X + XY) + \bar{X}(Y + \bar{Y}) = 1$. Because the distributive laws, the commutative laws and the associative laws hold in Boolean algebra, we can manipulate the left hand side exactly as we do in high school algebra. Then we get this sequence of equations:

$$X + XY + \bar{X}Y + \bar{X}\bar{Y} = 1$$
$$X + (X + \bar{X})Y + \bar{X}\bar{Y} = 1$$
$$X + 1 \cdot Y + \bar{X}\bar{Y} = 1$$
$$X + Y + \bar{X}\bar{Y} = 1$$

The last equation is the result we set out to get.

To show that the product of $X + Y$ and $\bar{X}\bar{Y}$ is equal to 0, multiply them, and then simplify as follows:

$$
\begin{aligned}
(X + Y)\bar{X}\bar{Y} &= X(\bar{X}\bar{Y}) + Y(\bar{X}\bar{Y}) \\
&= X(\bar{X}\bar{Y}) + Y(\bar{Y}\bar{X}) \\
&= (X\bar{X})\bar{Y} + (Y\bar{Y})\bar{X} \\
&= 0 \cdot \bar{Y} + 0 \cdot \bar{X} = 0 + 0 = 0.
\end{aligned}
$$

The second law of duality, which asserts that $\bar{X} + \bar{Y} = \overline{XY}$, can be proved by analogous argument.

We now use the law of duality to help us prove that if $C = AB$, then $\bar{A}B + A\bar{B} = (A + B)\bar{C}$:

$$
\begin{aligned}
\bar{A}B + A\bar{B} &= \bar{A}B + 0 + 0 + A\bar{B} \\
&= \bar{A}B + \bar{B}B + A\bar{A} + A\bar{B} \\
&= B(\bar{A} + \bar{B}) + A(\bar{A} + \bar{B}) \\
&= B(\overline{AB}) + A(\overline{AB}) \\
&= B\bar{C} + A\bar{C} \\
&= (B + A)\bar{C} = (A + B)\bar{C}.
\end{aligned}
$$

As a second consequence of the law of duality, we prove that $\overline{\overline{A}B + A\overline{B}} = AB + \overline{A}\overline{B}$. The law of duality says that the complement of a sum of two classes is the product of their complements. Then $\overline{\overline{A}B + A\overline{B}}$, which is the complement of the sum of $\overline{A}B$ and $A\overline{B}$, is equal to the product of the complement of $\overline{A}B$ and the complement of $A\overline{B}$. But, by the law of duality, the complement of a product of two classes is equal to the sum of their complements. So the complement of $\overline{A}B$ is equal to $A + \overline{B}$, and the complement of $A\overline{B}$ is equal to $\overline{A} + B$. Summarizing these observations, and then simplifying, we get this sequence of equalities:

$$\begin{aligned}
\overline{\overline{A}B + A\overline{B}} &= (\overline{\overline{A}B})(\overline{A\overline{B}}) \\
&= (A + \overline{B})(\overline{A} + B) \\
&= A\overline{A} + AB + \overline{B}\,\overline{A} + \overline{B}B \\
&= 0 + AB + \overline{A}\overline{B} + 0 \\
&= AB + \overline{A}\overline{B}.
\end{aligned}$$

A Census Problem

There are many practical situations in which we must deal with classes related to each other in complex ways. When the classes are described in words, it may be difficult to unravel the relationships among them. However, if Boolean algebra is used, expressing the relationships and solving relevant problems becomes a routine mathematical exercise. To show how Boolean algebra provides us with techniques for solving logical problems, we now apply it to three puzzle problems not much different from some of the problems that may arise in insurance, commerce, or industry.

The first problem we tackle is a census problem. In a high school with 100 students, a count was taken of the number of students taking science courses. The clerk who made the survey reported that there were 21 students taking biology, 40 students taking chemistry, 50 students taking physics, 11 students taking chemistry and physics, 9 students taking biology and physics, 20 students taking biology and chemistry, and 5 students taking biology, chemistry, and physics. After the principal of the school had studied the report, he threw it out and reprimanded the clerk. Why?

To see why, let us check the figures in the report for consistency. Let $B =$ the class of students taking biology, $C =$ the class of students taking chemistry, and $P =$ the class of students taking physics. Then $\bar{B} =$ the class of students not taking biology, $\bar{C} =$ the class of students not taking chemistry, and $\bar{P} =$ the class of students not taking physics. As usual, 1 stands for the universe class, which, in this case, is the class of all students in the school. If X is a class, let $n(X)$ denote the number of members of the class. Then the report of the clerk may be summarized as follows:

$$n(1) = 100. \qquad n(CP) = 11.$$
$$n(B) = 21. \qquad n(BP) = 9.$$
$$n(C) = 40. \qquad n(BC) = 20.$$
$$n(P) = 50. \qquad n(BCP) = 5.$$

We know that $B + \bar{B} = 1$. Multiplying by CP, we get $CP(B + \bar{B}) = (CP) \cdot 1$. Therefore, $CPB + CP\bar{B} = CP$. This equation expresses a decomposition of the class CP into two classes, CPB, and $CP\bar{B}$. Moreover, these two classes do not overlap, since $(CPB) \cdot (CP\bar{B}) = CCPP(B\bar{B})$ $= CP \cdot 0 = 0 =$ the empty class. Consequently, $n(CPB)$ $+ n(CP\bar{B}) = n(CP)$. But according to the survey report, $n(CPB)$, which is equal to $n(BCP)$, $= 5$, and $n(CP) = 11$. So $5 + n(CP\bar{B}) = 11$. We conclude then, that $n(CP\bar{B}) = 6$. Similarly, multiplying $C + \bar{C} = 1$ by BP, we get $BPC +$

$BP\bar{C} = BP$, and $n(BPC) + n(BP\bar{C}) = n(BP)$. Hence $5 + n(BC\bar{P}) = 20$, and $n(BC\bar{P}) = 15$. Now multiply the equation $(P + \bar{P})(C + \bar{C}) = 1$ by B. We get $B(P + \bar{P})(C + \bar{C}) = B$. Expanding the product on the left hand side of this equation, we get $BPC + BP\bar{C} + B\bar{P}C + B\bar{P}\bar{C} = B$. This equation expresses a decomposition of the class B into four classes. It is easy to see that no two of them overlap, since the product of any two of these classes is 0. Therefore it is necessary that $n(BPC) + n(BP\bar{C}) + n(B\bar{P}C) + n(B\bar{P}\bar{C}) = n(B)$. This equation requires that $5 + 4 + 15 + n(B\bar{P}\bar{C}) = 21$, which is impossible no matter how small the class $B\bar{P}\bar{C}$ may be. Therefore the figures in the clerk's report are inconsistent, and his survey was not accurate.

A Lewis Carroll Puzzle

Lewis Carroll, who is best known as the author of *Alice in Wonderland,* was a mathematician and logician. He made up many amusing logical problems for use as exercises in his textbook on *Symbolic Logic*. The next puzzle we solve is one of these exercises.

The problem is to find out what conclusion is a logical consequence of these ten propositions:

(1) The only animals in this house are cats;

(2) Every animal is suitable for a pet, that loves to gaze at the moon;

(3) When I detest an animal, I avoid it;

(4) No animals are carnivorous, unless they prowl at night;

(5) No cat fails to kill mice;

(6) No animals ever take to me, except what are in this house;

(7) Kangaroos are not suitable for pets;
(8) None but carnivora kill mice;
(9) I detest animals that do not take to me;
(10) Animals that prowl at night always love to gaze at the moon.

To solve this problem by Boolean algebra, we first introduce symbols for various classes:

Let 1 = the universe class = the class of all animals
A = the class of animals avoided by me
B = the class of carnivora
C = the class of cats
D = the class of animals detested by me
E = the class of animals in this house
H = the class of kangaroos
K = the class of animals that kill mice
L = the class of animals that love to gaze at the moon
M = the class of animals that prowl at night
N = the class of animals that are suitable for pets
R = the class of animals that take to me

Expressed in terms of these symbols, the ten propositions take this form:

(1) $EC = E$ (6) $RE = R$
(2) $LN = L$ (7) $H\bar{N} = H$
(3) $DA = D$ (8) $KB = K$
(4) $BM = B$ (9) $\bar{R}D = \bar{R}$
(5) $CK = C$ (10) $ML = M$

Now we develop a chain of equations as follows: Multiply equation (1) by R, to get $R(EC) = RE$. Using the associative law of multiplication, this can be rewritten as $(RE)C = RE$. By equation (6), RE may be replaced by R. So we get as equation (11), $RC = R$. Multiply equation (5) by R, and use the associative law, to get $(RC)K = RC$.

By equation (11), RC may be replaced by R. So we get as equation (12), $RK = R$. Multiply equation (8) by R, and use the associative law, to get $(RK)B = RK$. By equation (12), RK may be replaced by R. So we get as equation (13), $RB = R$. Multiply equation (4) by R, and use the associative law, to get $(RB)M = RB$. By equation (13), RB may be replaced by R. So we get as equation (14), $RM = R$. Multiply equation (10) by R, and use the associative law, to get $(RM)L = RM$. By equation (14), RM may be replaced by R. So we get as equation (15), $RL = R$. Multiply equation (2) by R, and use the associative law, to get $(RL)N = RL$. By equation (15), RL may be replaced by R. So we get as equation (16), $RN = R$. Multiply equation (7) by R. This gives us $R(H\bar{N}) = RH$. By equation (16), we may replace the R on the left by RN, to get $(RN)(H\bar{N}) = RH$. Using the associative and commutative laws of multiplication to rearrange the order and regroup the factors on the left, we get $(N\bar{N})(RH) = RH$. But $N\bar{N} = 0$, so we get $0(RH) = RH$, and hence $RH = 0$. We know that $R + \bar{R} = 1$. If we multiply this equation by H, we get $HR + H\bar{R} = H$. But $HR = RH = 0$, so it follows that $H\bar{R} = H$, and we call this equation (17). Multiply equation (9) by H, and use the associative law, to get $(H\bar{R})D = H\bar{R}$. By equation (17), we may replace $H\bar{R}$ by H. So we get as equation (18), $HD = H$. Multiply equation (3) by H, and use the associative law, to get $(HD)A = HD$. By equation (18), we may replace HD by H. Our final result is that $HA = H$. This is equivalent to the statement that $H \subset A$. The conclusion from propositions (1) to (10), therefore, is the proposition, *I always avoid kangaroos.*

Who Is the Engineer?

The third puzzle that we solve by means of Boolean alegbra is a brain twister that is well known to puzzle fans. Here is one of the many versions of it. For convenience, we number the separate statements that are made.

(1) Smith, Jones and Robinson are the conductor, brakeman, and the engineer on a train, but not necessarily in that order.

(2) There are three passengers on the train named Mr. Smith, Mr. Jones, and Mr. Robinson. We shall use the title *Mister* only when we refer to one of these passengers.

(3) The conductor lives in Manhattan.

(4) The conductor's namesake (the passenger who has the same name as the conductor) lives in Philadelphia.

(5) Mr. Jones earns $10,000 per year.

(6) Mr. Robinson lives in Queens.

(7) One of the three passengers is the conductor's next-door neighbor.

(8) The conductor earns in cash each year exactly one third of the salary of his next-door neighbor.

(9) Smith beats the brakeman at billiards.

The problem is, who is the engineer?

In the solution given below, after defining the symbols that are used, we give only a sequence of equations. The reader should be able to justify each equation by referring to information already known and to some relevant axioms or theorems. (Keep in mind that if X is a subclass of Y, $XY = X$, and that if X and Y have no common members, $XY = 0$.)

Let S = the unit class whose member is Smith
$\quad\; J$ = the unit class whose member is Jones
$\quad\; R$ = the unit class whose member is Robinson
$\quad\; C$ = the unit class whose member is the conductor
$\quad\; B$ = the unit class whose member is the brakeman
$\quad\; E$ = the unit class whose member is the engineer
$\quad\; C'$ = the unit class whose member is the conductor's namesake
$\quad\; S'$ = the unit class whose member is Mr. Smith
$\quad\; J'$ = the unit class whose member is Mr. Jones
$\quad\; R'$ = the unit class whose member is Mr. Robinson
$\quad\; T$ = the class of all people earning \$10,000 per year
$\quad\; M$ = the class of all people living in Manhattan
$\quad\; P$ = the class of all people living in Philadelphia
$\quad\; Q$ = the class of all people living in Queens
$\quad\; C''$ = the unit class whose member is the conductor's next-door neighbor

$S + J + R = C + B + E.$

$SJ = 0,\ SR = 0,\ \text{and}\ JR = 0.$

$CM = C.$ Therefore $CP = 0$ and $CQ = 0.$

$C'P = C'.$ Therefore $C'M = 0$ and $C'Q = 0.$

$R'Q = R'.$ Therefore $R'M = 0,$ and $R'P = 0.$

$J'T = J'.\ SB = 0.$

$C''M = C''.$ Therefore $C''P = 0,$ and $C''Q = 0.$

$C''(S' + J' + R') = C''.\ C''T = 0.$

$C''(S' + J'T + R') = C''.$

$C''S' + C''J'T + C''R' = C''.$

Therefore $C''S' + C''R' = C''.$

$M(C''S' + C''R') = MC''.$

$MC''S' + MC''R' = MC''.$

Therefore $C''S' = C'',$ hence $C'' = S',$ and $S'P = 0.$

$C'(S' + J' + R') = C'.$

$C'S' + C'J' + C'R' = C'.$

$P(C'S' + C'J' + C'R') = PC'.$

$C'(S'P) + (C'P)J' + C'(R'P) = PC'.$

Therefore $C'J' = C'$, hence $C' = J'$, and $C = J$.

But if $C = J$, $SC = SJ = 0$.

$S(C + B + E) = S$.

$SC + SB + SE = S$. Therefore $SE = S$, and $S = E$.

That is, *Smith is the engineer.*

CHAPTER 9

Algebra of Propositions

Propositions about Propositions

EVERY proposition is either true or false. The typical job of a scientist is to determine whether certain propositions are true or false. The propositions always concern the subject matter of his science. The biologist tries to separate the true from the false among propositions about plants and animals and their relations to each other and the environment. The chemist tries to separate the true from the false among propositions about chemical elements and their compounds. The physicist tries to separate the true from the false among propositions about matter and energy.

The logician, too, seeks the truth value of propositions about his subject matter. An important part of the science of logic is concerned with propositions, and their relations to each other. So the logician tries to separate the true from the false among *propositions about propositions*.

Here is a typical proposition that may come up in the study of logic: If it is true that if it is raining, then the ground is wet, and if it is true that if the ground is wet, then your shoes get wet, then it is also true that if it is raining, then your shoes get wet. This is a rather complicated proposition built up out of simpler propositions. The simpler propositions are: It is raining; the ground is wet; your shoes get wet. They are joined together in the complicated proposition by the words "if . . . then" and the word "and." The latter are called *connectives*. The set of words "if . . . then" can be replaced by the word "implies." Thus, the part of the proposition that says, ". . . if it is raining, then the

96

ground is wet," can be replaced by, "*It is raining* implies that *the ground is wet.*" In order to reveal the structure of the complicated proposition more clearly, let us use the letter p to stand for the proposition "It is raining." Let q stand for "The ground is wet." Let r stand for "Your shoes get wet." Then the proposition says "If p implies q, and q implies r, then p implies r." You will recognize that this proposition merely asserts the transitive property of the relation "implies," so that it is true, no matter what propositions p, q, and r stand for. The truth of this proposition depends only on its form. One of the major goals of the logician is to discover propositions of precisely this kind. Since, for his purposes, p, q, and r may stand for any propositions whatever, it is better for him to make his assertions in terms of such variables, rather than about specific propositions.

Symbols for Truth Values

Following the lead of the logician, we shall use small letters like p, q, and r as variables that stand for propositions, just as in elementary algebra we use letters like x, y and z as variables that stand for numbers. As long as we shall be using symbols for propositions, we may as well use symbols to stand for their truth values. Let us agree to use the symbol *1* for *true*, and the symbol *0* for *false*. Let us agree, too, that whenever a small letter stands for a proposition, the corresponding capital letter stands for its truth value. Thus, if p stands for a proposition, then P stands for its truth value. While p may stand for any proposition whatever, P may take on only two values, 1 and 0. If p is the proposition, "All men are mortal," then $P = 1$. If p is the proposition, "The area of a circle equals twice the square of its radius," then $P = 0$.

Symbols for Connectives

The connectives "if . . . then" and "and" enable us to form new, compound propositions from old propositions. Other connectives that serve the same purpose are the words, "or," "not," and "if and only if." We now give the meaning of each of these connectives, and introduce a convenient symbol for it.

Or. Let p and q be propositions. Then the proposition p *or* q is the proposition that asserts that at least one of the propositions p and q is true. We shall use a plus sign to stand for *or*, so p *or* q will be written as $p + q$. For example, if p stands for the proposition "it is raining," and q stands for the proposition "the ground is wet," then $p + q$ stands for the proposition, "Either it is raining, or the ground is wet, or it is raining and the ground is wet." The proposition $p + q$ is called the *disjunction* of p and q.

And. The proposition p *and* q is the proposition that asserts that both p and q are true. We shall use a multiplication sign (usually omitted) to stand for *and*, so that p *and* q will be written as pq. If p stands for "it is raining," and q stands for "the ground is wet," then pq stands for, "It is raining and the ground is wet." The proposition pq is called the *conjunction* of p and q.

Not. The proposition *not* p is the proposition that asserts that p is not true. We shall use the symbol $\sim$ for *not,* so that *not* p will be written as $\sim p$. If p stands for "it is raining," then $\sim p$ stands for, "It is not true that it is raining," or, more briefly, "It is not raining." The proposition $\sim p$ is called the *negation* of p.

If . . . then. The proposition *if* p, *then* q is the proposition that asserts that if p is false, q may be true or false, but if p is true, then q is true. We shall use a single-headed arrow to stand for *if . . . then,* so that *if* p, *then* q will be written as $p \rightarrow q$. The proposition $p \rightarrow q$ is called the *conditional* of p and q.

If and only if. The proposition p *if and only if* q is the proposition that asserts that p and q are either both true or both false. We shall use a double-headed arrow to stand for *if and only if*, so that *p if and only if q* will be written as $p \longleftrightarrow q$. The proposition $p \longleftrightarrow q$ is called the *biconditional of p and q*.

Truth Tables

The expression $p + q$ is not a proposition. It is only a propositional form. It becomes a proposition when p and q are replaced by specific propositions. The truth value of the proposition that results depends on the truth values of the propositions that replace p and q. Let us write $P + Q$ for the truth value of $p + q$. By definition, $p + q$ is true if either p or q or both are true. Otherwise $p + q$ is false. Therefore, $P + Q = 1$ if $P = 1$, or $Q = 1$, or $P = Q = 1$. Otherwise, $P + Q = 0$. These facts may be conveniently summarized in the following *truth table*, which shows the truth value for $p + q$ for all possible combinations of truth values for p and q:

P	Q	$P + Q$
1 (*p* is true)	1 (*q* is true)	1 (*p or q* is true)
1 (*p* is true)	0 (*q* is false)	1 (*p or q* is true)
0 (*p* is false)	1 (*q* is true)	1 (*p or q* is true)
0 (*p* is false)	0 (*q* is false)	0 (*p or q* is false)

Let us write PQ for the truth value of pq, $\sim P$ for the truth value of $\sim p$, $P \rightarrow Q$ for the truth value of $p \rightarrow q$, and $P \longleftrightarrow Q$ for the truth value of $p \longleftrightarrow q$. The truth tables for these propositional forms are easily constructed on the basis of the definitions given above.

P	Q	PQ
1	1	1
1	0	0
0	1	0
0	0	0

P	$\sim P$
1	0
0	1

P	Q	$P \to Q$
1	1	1
1	0	0
0	1	1
0	0	1

P	Q	$P \leftrightarrow Q$
1	1	1
1	0	0
0	1	0
0	0	1

Using these five basic truth tables, we can construct the truth tables for more complicated propositional forms that use more than one connective. For example, to find all possible truth values of $(\sim p) + q$, corresponding to all combinations of truth values of p and q, we use the truth tables for $\sim p$, and for $p + q$. List the combinations of values for P and Q in the first two columns. In the third column, list the value of $\sim P$ that corresponds to each value of P. When $P = 1$, $\sim P = 0$, and vice versa. Then, in the fourth column, list the values of $(\sim P) + Q$ that correspond to the combinations of values of $\sim P$ and Q. $P + Q = 0$ only when $P = Q = 0$. $P + Q = 1$ in all other cases. Therefore, $(\sim P) + Q = 0$ only when $\sim P = Q = 0$. Otherwise $(\sim P) + Q = 1$.

P	Q	$\sim P$	$(\sim P) + Q$
1	1	0	1
1	0	0	0
0	1	1	1
0	0	1	1

Equivalent Propositional Forms

In the preceding table, we used the third column only to help us calculate the entries in the fourth column. Now that it has served its purpose, we may disregard it. The complete truth table for $(\sim p) + q$ is given by columns 1, 2, and 4. Comparing these with the three columns in the truth table for $p \to q$, we see that the truth table for $p \to q$ is exactly the same as the truth table for $(\sim p) + q$. When two propositional forms have the same truth table, we say they are *equivalent*. Equivalent forms are either true together, or false together. Hence if X and Y are equivalent, $X \longleftrightarrow Y$. Therefore the symbol $\longleftrightarrow$ may be read as "is equivalent to."

To calculate all possible truth values of $\sim (\sim p)$, prepare a table with three columns, as shown below. In the first column, put all possible truth values of p. In the second column, put the corresponding truth values of $\sim p$. They are the opposite of the truth values of p. That is, when $p = 0$, $\sim p = 1$, and vice versa. In the third column, put the truth values of $\sim (\sim p)$. They are the opposite of the truth values of $\sim p$. Now compare the third column with the first column. They are exactly the same. In other words, p and $\sim (\sim p)$ have the same truth tables. Therefore p is equivalent to $\sim (\sim p)$. That is, $p \longleftrightarrow \sim (\sim p)$. This is the familiar rule of the "double negative."

P	$\sim P$	$\sim(\sim P)$
1	0	1
0	1	0

To calculate all possible truth values of $(p \to q) \cdot (q \to p)$, which we read as "$p$ implies q, and q implies p," prepare a table with five columns. In the first two columns put all possible combinations of truth values of the two propositions p and q. In the third column, put the corresponding truth values of $p \to q$. $P \to Q$ is 0 when $P = 1$ and $Q = 0$. Otherwise it is 1. In the fourth column, put the corresponding truth values of $q \to p$. $Q \to P$ is 0 when $Q = 1$ and $P = 0$. Otherwise it is 1. In the fifth column, put the corresponding truth values of $(p \to q) (q \to p)$. The value is 1 when the value appearing in columns 3 and 4 is 1. In all other cases, the value is 0.

P	Q	$P \to Q$	$Q \to P$	$(P \to Q)(Q \to P)$
1	1	1	1	1
1	0	0	1	0
0	1	1	0	0
0	0	1	1	1

If we compare the first, second and fifth columns of this table with the table for $p \longleftrightarrow q$, we see that $p \longleftrightarrow q$ is equivalent to $(p \to q) (q \to p)$. That is why $p \longleftrightarrow q$ is called the biconditional.

As a practice exercise, show that the propositional form $pq \longleftrightarrow p$ is equivalent to $p \to q$.

Reducing the Number of Connectives

When two propositional forms are equivalent, they have the same truth values no matter what propositions are substituted for the variables that appear in the forms. To express this fact, we put an "equals" sign between the expressions for their truth values. Thus, since p is equivalent to $\sim (\sim p)$, we say $P = \sim (\sim P)$. Since $p \to q$ is equivalent to $(\sim p) + q$, we say $P \to Q = (\sim P) + Q$. Since $p \longleftrightarrow q$ is equivalent to $(p \to q) (q \to p)$, we say $P \longleftrightarrow Q = (P \to Q) (Q \to P)$. Moreover, when two propositional forms always have the same truth values, it means that they have the same truth tables, and must be equivalent. So a statement that two propositional forms are equivalent is interchangeable with the statement that the expressions for their truth values are equal.

In the expressions for truth values that we have examined, five different connectives appear. It is now possible for us to reduce the number to three. Since $P \rightarrow Q = (\sim P) + Q$, we can always replace $P \rightarrow Q$ by $(\sim P) + Q$. In this way we replace an expression using the connective $\rightarrow$ by an expression using the connectives $\sim$ and $+$. Since $P \longleftrightarrow Q = (P \rightarrow Q)(Q \rightarrow P)$, then, making the appropriate substitutions, we have $P \longleftrightarrow Q = [(\sim P) + Q] \cdot [(\sim Q) + P]$. So any expression using the connective $\longleftrightarrow$ can be replaced by an expression using the connectives $\sim$, $\cdot$ and $+$. By means of these substitutions, all expressions using our five original connectives are transformed into expressions using only the three connectives, *not, and* and *or*.

The Algebra of Propositions

The words *not, and* and *or* have come up before in another context. In Chapter VIII, where we explored the algebra of classes, the word *not* was the key word in defining the operation of taking the complement of a class. The word *and* was the key word in the operation we called multiplication. The word *or* was the key word in the operation we called addition. Complementation, multiplication, and addition are the three basic operations of the Boolean algebra of classes. This suggests the possibility of having an algebra of propositions. We already have at hand all the materials needed for constructing such an algebra. As the system of elements that make up the algebra we shall use the *truth values* of propositions. For basic operations in the algebra, we use the connectives *not, and* and *or*, denoted by the symbols $\sim$, $\cdot$, and $+$. We already have tables for these three operations in the form of truth tables:

P	Q	$P+Q$
1	1	1
1	0	1
0	1	1
0	0	0

P	Q	PQ
1	1	1
1	0	0
0	1	0
0	0	0

P	$\sim P$
1	0
0	1

The first two tables can be recast in another form in which the values of P are written at the left hand side, and the values of Q are written at the top. This is the form usually used for addition and multiplication tables:

+	1	0
1	1	1
0	1	0

·	1	0
1	1	0
0	0	0

P	$\sim P$
1	0
0	1

If we compare these tables with those on page 83, we see that they are precisely the tables for a two-valued Boolean algebra, with disjunction taking the place of addition, conjunction taking the place of multiplication, and negation taking the place of complementation. Consequently, the *algebra of propositions is a Boolean algebra*. This means that all the axioms and theorems of Boolean algebra are true statements about the truth values of propositions. It is understood, of course, that in making such statements, we must replace every expression like $\bar{X}$ by the analogous expression $\sim X$.

Now that we know that the algebra of propositions is a Boolean algebra, we have a way of identifying equivalent propositional forms without constructing their truth tables. Two propositional forms are equivalent, if we can transform the expression for the truth value of one into the expression for the truth value of the other by the laws of Boolean algebra. For example, one of the distributive laws says that $P(Q + R) = PQ + PR$. Therefore $p(q + r)$ and $pq + pr$ must have the same truth table. This fact is verified directly in the truth tables below. Notice that we need eight lines in each of these truth tables to take into account the eight possible combinations of truth values of the three propositions p, q, and r.

P	Q	R	Q + R	P(Q + R)
1	1	1	1	1
1	1	0	1	1
1	0	1	1	1
1	0	0	0	0
0	1	1	1	0
0	1	0	1	0
0	0	1	1	0
0	0	0	0	0

P	Q	R	PQ	PR	PQ + PR
1	1	1	1	1	1
1	1	0	1	0	1
1	0	1	0	1	1
1	0	0	0	0	0
0	1	1	0	0	0
0	1	0	0	0	0
0	0	1	0	0	0
0	0	0	0	0	0

The law of duality says that $\sim (P + Q) = (\sim P)(\sim Q)$. As a practice exercise, verify that $\sim(p + q)$ and $(\sim p)(\sim q)$ have the same truth tables.

Tautologies

There are some propositional forms that always have the truth value 1 no matter what propositions are substituted for the variables that appear in the forms. Such forms are easily recognized by the fact that only 1's appear in the last column of their truth tables. We call these forms *tautologies*. If we join two equivalent propositional forms by the connective $\longleftrightarrow$, the resulting form is a tautology. This fact is verified directly in the truth table below for the propositional form $(p \rightarrow q) \longleftrightarrow (pq \longleftrightarrow p)$. In this table, an entry in the fifth column is 1 only when the corresponding entries in the first and fourth column are the same. (See the definition of $\longleftrightarrow$ on page 99.) An entry in the sixth column is 1 only when the corresponding entries in the third and fifth columns are the same.

P	Q	$P \rightarrow Q$	PQ	$PQ \leftrightarrow P$	$(P \rightarrow Q) \leftrightarrow (PQ \leftrightarrow P)$
1	1	1	1	1	1
1	0	0	0	0	1
0	1	1	0	1	1
0	0	1	0	1	1

Valid and Invalid Reasoning

Tautologies play an important part in deductive reasoning. A deductive argument is made up of a string of assertions in which we say that if certain propositions are true, then some other proposition is also true as a consequence. Each of these assertions is itself a proposition. If we replace the propositions within it by variables, the result is a propositional form. The reasoning is logical, and we say the argument is *valid*, if and only if each of the propositional forms obtained is a tautology, For example, let us consider the argument written out on pages 96 and 97. As we pointed out there, the structure of the argument is embodied in the propositional form, *if p implies q, and q implies r, then p implies r.* Using the symbol $\rightarrow$ for *implies*, we can write the argument more briefly in this form: if $p \rightarrow q$, and $q \rightarrow r$, then $p \rightarrow r$. We can abbreviate it even further by writing $\rightarrow$ for *if . . . then,* and $\cdot$ for *and.* In purely symbolic form, the argument looks like this: $(p \rightarrow q)(q \rightarrow r) \rightarrow (p \rightarrow r)$. The truth table for this form shows that it is a tautology:

P	Q	R	P → Q	Q → R	(P → Q)(Q → R)	P → R	(P → Q)(Q → R) → (P → R)
1	1	1	1	1	1	1	1
1	1	0	1	0	0	0	1
1	0	1	0	1	0	1	1
1	0	0	0	1	0	0	1
0	1	1	1	1	1	1	1
0	1	0	1	0	0	1	1
0	0	1	1	1	1	1	1
0	0	0	1	1	1	1	1

When the form of an argument is not a tautology, the argument is fallacious, and really does not prove what it claims to prove. It is not always easy to recognize a fallacious argument when it is expressed in words. But it can always be exposed by constructing the truth table of the underlying propositional form. As an example, let us analyze an argument that is frequently heard in the United States. The argument runs as follows: If a man is a communist, then he criticizes the government's foreign policy. This man criticizes the government's foreign policy. Therefore he is a communist. The propositional form underlying this argument is: If $(p \rightarrow q)$ and q, then p. Expressing it all in symbols, we have $(p \rightarrow q) q \rightarrow p$. The truth table for this propositional form, constructed below, has a 0 in the last column, so the form is not a tautology. Hence the argument is fallacious.

P	Q	P → Q	(P → Q)Q	(P → Q) Q → P
1	1	1	1	1
1	0	0	0	1
0	1	1	1	0
0	0	1	0	1

Another way of expressing the same argument is this: $p \rightarrow q$ is equivalent to $q \rightarrow p$. People are tempted to accept this as a true statement because of the superficial resemblance between the two conditionals. However, the truth tables below show that these forms are not equivalent.

P	Q	$P \rightarrow Q$		P	Q	$Q \rightarrow P$
1	1	1		1	1	1
1	0	0		1	0	1
0	1	1		0	1	0
0	0	1		0	0	1

The form $q \rightarrow p$ is called the converse of $p \rightarrow q$. While the converse of $p \rightarrow q$ is not equivalent to it, there is another propositional form that is. The form $(\sim q) \rightarrow (\sim p)$, which is known as the *contrapositive* of $p \rightarrow q$, is equivalent to $p \rightarrow q$. As an exercise, verify this fact by constructing their truth tables.

A Form for a Truth Table

A truth table can be constructed for any given propositional form. The process can also be reversed. Given any truth table, it is possible to find a propositional form that has that truth table. There is a simple procedure for constructing the form. The best way to explain the procedure is to demonstrate it in connection with a specific problem.

Problem: Construct a three-variable propositional form that has the truth table appearing on page 109.

Procedure: First we construct eight forms, each corresponding to one of the lines in the table. Each

P	Q	R	Truth Value of Required Form
1	1	1	1
1	1	0	1
1	0	1	0
1	0	0	1
0	1	1	0
0	1	0	1
0	0	1	0
0	0	0	1

form is the product (conjunction) of three factors. The first factor is p or $\sim p$, depending on whether $P = 1$ or 0. The second factor is q or $\sim q$, depending on whether $Q = 1$ or 0. The third factor is r or $\sim r$, depending on whether $R = 1$ or 0. Thus the form corresponding to the first line is pqr; the form for the second line is $pq(\sim r)$; the form for the third line is $p(\sim q)r$; etc. We get the required form by taking the sum (disjunction) of some of these forms. We use only those forms that correspond to a line where the value 1 appears in the last column of the table. The required form for this table is: $pqr + pq(\sim r) + p(\sim q)(\sim r) + (\sim p)q(\sim r) + (\sim p)(\sim q)(\sim r)$.

We have seen that it is possible for different forms to have the same truth table. So a given table belongs, in general, to many forms. The procedure described above gives only one of them. However, other equivalent forms can be obtained from it by using the rules of Boolean algebra. First write the expression for the truth value of the form. This simply means rewrite it with capital letters instead of small letters. Transform this expression into a new one according to the rules of Boolean algebra. Then get the form that belongs to the new expression by simply rewriting it with small letters. The practical purpose of all this work would be to get a simpler form than the original one. For example, the truth value for the form we constructed for the table is $PQR + PQ(\sim R) + P(\sim Q)(\sim R) + (\sim P)Q(\sim R) + (\sim P)(\sim Q)(\sim R)$. By the rules of Boolean algebra, this expression is equal to:

$$PQ(R + \sim R) + P(\sim Q)(\sim R) + (\sim P)(\sim R)(Q + \sim Q).$$

But $R + \sim R = 1$, and $Q + \sim Q = 1$, so the expression is equal to $PQ \cdot 1 + P(\sim Q)(\sim R) + (\sim P)(\sim R) 1$, which in turn is equal to $PQ + P(\sim Q)(\sim R) + (\sim P)(\sim R)$. This gives us the simpler propositional form $pq + p(\sim q)(\sim r) + (\sim p)(\sim r)$ as another solution to the problem.

In the search for equivalent propositional forms, we can take a short-cut by manipulating the propositional forms themselves instead of the expressions for their truth values. This is legitimate because it merely means skipping the steps in which we change from small letters to capital letters, and then back again to small letters. When the short-cut is used, we would say $p + \sim p = 1$, although, strictly speaking, the correct statement is that $P + \sim P = 1$.

The technique for constructing a propositional form for a given truth table has important practical applications. In Chapter XI we shall have occasion to use it for designing some basic components of an electronic computer. Meanwhile, we shall use it now to solve a well-known logical puzzle.

Puzzle: A logician once visited a country inhabited by two tribes, the Saints and the Sinners. The Saints and the Sinners look alike, dress alike, and have the same speech pattern, so that they cannot be distinguished by any outward signs. However, they differ in one important respect. The Saints always tell the truth, while the Sinners always lie. Once, while the logician was traveling on foot to the city Metropolis, he came to a fork in the road. There were no road signs to indicate which branch of the road led to the city. However, there was a native standing at the fork at the time. The logician, of course, did not know whether he was a Saint or a Sinner, so he could not count on a truthful answer to any question he might ask. Nevertheless, he asked the native a single question, and found out from the answer which branch of the road he should take. What was the question?

A solution to the puzzle can be worked out as follows. Since there are two branches that the logician must choose from, his question should permit only two answers. This requirement is met if his question calls for *yes* or *no* as an answer. He should frame the question in such a way that the answer will be *yes* if the left branch is the road to the city, and will be *no* if the right branch is the road to the city, whether the native tells the truth, or not. To construct such a question, first denote by *p* the statement, "The left branch is the road to Metropolis," and denote by *q* the statement, "You are a Saint." Now construct a table with four columns. In the first two columns list all possible combinations of truth values to *p* and *q*. In the third column list the answer the logician wants to get to his question. It will depend on the truth value of *p*. Express the answer in code by writing 1 for *yes* and 0 for *no*. In the fourth column, put down what appears in the third column on lines where $Q = 1$. Where $Q = 0$, make the entry in the fourth column the opposite of the entry in the third column. The fourth column will give the truth values of an unknown compound propositional form. Here is the table:

P	Q	*Answer Wanted*	*Unknown Form*
1	1	1	1
1	0	1	0
0	1	0	0
0	0	0	1

A propositional form that has the truth values shown in the last column is $pq + (\sim p)(\sim q)$. If the logician asks "Is $pq + (\sim p)(\sim q)$ true?", the answer, no matter what the circumstances shown in columns 1 and 2, will be the one indicated in column 3. So, the appropriate question, expressed in words, is this: Is it true that either the left branch is the road to Metropolis and you are a Saint, or the left branch is not the road to Metropolis and you are a Sinner?

Boolean Algebra in Medicine

We close this chapter on the algebra of propositions by describing one of its most interesting applications. We show how Boolean algebra can be used to make a medical diagnosis.

When a doctor examines a patient, he looks for certain symptoms. His observations take the form of propositions: the patient has this symptom; he doesn't have that symptom; etc. The doctor also has medical knowledge. His knowledge is a collection of propositions about how symptoms and diseases are related. His diagnosis is a logical deduction from the two sets of propositions.

Let us assume that there are two symptoms s and t, each of which is either present or absent. Let us denote by s the proposition, *the patient has symptom s*. Then $\sim s$ denotes the proposition, *the patient does not have symptom s*. Let t denote the proposition, *the patient has symptom t*. Then $\sim t$ means *the patient does not have symptom t*.

Let us assume that there are two diseases, c and d. Denote by c the proposition, *the patient has disease c*. Denote by d the proposition, *the patient has disease d*. Assume that the state of medical knowledge about these diseases is embodied in these propositions:

1) If the patient has disease d, he must have symptom s.
2) If the patient has disease c and not disease d, he must have symptom t.

3) If the patient has disease d and not disease c, he cannot have symptom t.
4) If the patient has symptom s or t or both, then he must have either disease c or disease d or both.

What is the diagnosis if the patient has symptom t but does not have symptom s?

The first step in solving this problem is to express propositions 1 to 4 in symbolic form:

1) $d \rightarrow s$.   2) $c(\sim d) \rightarrow t$.   3) $d(\sim c) \rightarrow \sim t$.
4) $s + t \rightarrow c + d$.

On page 102, we mentioned that the form $p \rightarrow q$ is equivalent to the form $pq \longleftrightarrow p$. So the four propositions may be expressed just as well in this way:

1) $ds \longleftrightarrow d$.   2) $c(\sim d)t \longleftrightarrow c(\sim d)$.
3) $d(\sim c)(\sim t) \longleftrightarrow d(\sim c)$.   4) $(s + t)(c + d) \longleftrightarrow (s + t)$.

Equivalent propositions have equal truth values. So the last four propositions lead to these equations about truth values:

$$\text{I) } DS = D.$$
$$\text{II) } C(\sim D)T = C(\sim D).$$
$$\text{III) } D(\sim C)(\sim T) = D(\sim C).$$
$$\text{IV) } (S + T)(C + D) = S + T.$$

From now on, we work only with truth values. Multiplying equation I by $\sim S$, we get $DS(\sim S) = D(\sim S)$. But $S(\sim S) = 0$. Therefore $D(\sim S) = 0$. Similarly, from equation II we get $C(\sim D)(\sim T) = 0$, and from equation III we get $D(\sim C)T = 0$. From equation IV we get $(S + T)[\sim(C + D)] = 0$.

We know that $S + \sim S = 1$, and $T + \sim T = 1$. Multiplying these two equations we get $(S + \sim S)(T + \sim T) = 1$. Expanding the left hand member, we get: $ST + S(\sim T) + (\sim S)T + (\sim S)(\sim T) = 1$. Similarly, from $C + \sim C = 1$, and $D + \sim D = 1$, we get $CD + C(\sim D) +$

$(\sim C)D + (\sim C)\ (\sim D) = 1$. Multiplying the two expanded equations, we get:

$$[ST + S(\sim T) + (\sim S)T + (\sim S)(\sim T)] \cdot$$
$$[CD + C(\sim D) + (\sim C)D + (\sim C)(\sim D)] = 1.$$

This equation, in expanded form, asserts:

$$STCD + STC(\sim D) + ST(\sim C)D + ST(\sim C)(\sim D) +$$
$$S(\sim T)CD + S(\sim T)C(\sim D) + S(\sim T)(\sim C)D +$$
$$S(\sim T)(\sim C)(\sim D) + (\sim S)TCD + (\sim S)TC(\sim D) +$$
$$(\sim S)T(\sim C)D + (\sim S)T(\sim C)(\sim D) + (\sim S)(\sim T)$$
$$CD + (\sim S)(\sim T)C(\sim D) + (\sim S)(\sim T)(\sim C)D +$$
$$(\sim S)(\sim T)(\sim C)(\sim D) = 1.$$

Because $D(\sim S) = 0$, the 9th, 11th, 13th and 15th terms on the left hand side are equal to 0. Because $C(\sim D)\ (\sim T) = 0$, the 6th and the 14th terms are equal to 0. Because $D(\sim C)T = 0$, the third term is 0. So all these terms drop out of the equation, and we get:

$$STCD + STC(\sim D) + ST(\sim C)(\sim D) + S(\sim T)CD +$$
$$S(\sim T)(\sim C)D + S(\sim T)(\sim C)(\sim D) + (\sim S)TC(\sim D)$$
$$+ (\sim S)T(\sim C)(\sim D) + (\sim S)(\sim T)(\sim C)(\sim D) = 1.$$

We can simplify this equation further by making use of the equation $(S + T)\ [\sim(C + D)] = 0$ which we had derived from IV. By the law of duality $\sim(C + D) = (\sim C)(\sim D)$. So we have

$(S + T)(\sim C)(\sim D) = 0$. Hence $S(\sim C)(\sim D) + T(\sim C)(\sim D) = 0$.

The addition table for the two-valued Boolean algebra shows that the sum of two terms is 0 only if each term is itself 0. Therefore $S(\sim C)\ (\sim D) = 0$, and $T(\sim C)\ (\sim D) = 0$. So three more terms drop out of the equation, and we have:

$$STCD + STC(\sim D) + S(\sim T)CD + S(\sim T)(\sim C)D +$$
$$(\sim S)TC(\sim D) + (\sim S)(\sim T)(\sim C)(\sim D) = 1.$$

Using the distributive law to rewrite terms 1 and 2, and also terms 3 and 4, we get:

$STC(D + \sim D) + S(\sim T)D(C + \sim C) + (\sim S)TC(\sim D) + (\sim S)(\sim T)(\sim C)(\sim D) = 1$. Since $D + \sim D = 1$, and $C + \sim C = 1$, we finally get: $STC + S(\sim T)D + (\sim S)TC(\sim D) + (\sim S)(\sim T)(\sim C)(\sim D) = 1$.

This last equation summarizes the state of medical knowledge concerning the relationship between diseases c and d and symptoms s and t. Let us call it equation *MK*.

If the patient has symptom t, but not s, then $T = 1$, $\sim T = 0$, $S = 0$, and $\sim S = 1$. Making these substitutions into equation *MK*, we get:

$$0 \cdot 1 \cdot C + 0 \cdot 0 \cdot D + 1 \cdot 1 \cdot C(\sim D) + 1 \cdot 0 \cdot (\sim C)(\sim D) = 1.$$

This reduces to $C(\sim D) = 1$. This is true if and only if $C = 1$ and $\sim D = 1$. Therefore the diagnosis is: The patient has disease c, but not disease d.

Suppose the patient has symptom s, but not t. What is the diagnosis then? Under these circumstances, $S = 1$, $\sim S = 0$, $T = 0$, and $\sim T = 1$. Making these substitutions into equation *MK*, we get:

$$1 \cdot 0 \cdot C + 1 \cdot 1 \cdot D + 0 \cdot 0 \cdot C(\sim D) + 0 \cdot 1(\sim C)(\sim D) = 1.$$

This reduces to $D = 1$. Therefore the diagnosis is: The patient has disease d. However, the diagnosis is incomplete, because it does not say whether or not the patient also has disease c. The medical knowledge expressed in equation *MK* is inadequate for settling this question.

CHAPTER 10

Switching Circuits

An Algebra of Switches

IN THE diagram below we show an electrical appliance in a line joined to the terminals of an electrical power supply. The switch S is used to control the current through the appliance. When the switch is closed, the current is on. When the switch is open, the current is off.

The two possible states of a switch, closed or open, are analogous to the two possible truth values of a proposition, true or false. The resemblance prompts us to introduce symbols to represent these states. Let 1 stand for the state of being closed, and let 0 stand for the state of being open.

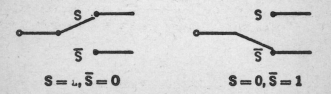

$$S = 1, \bar{S} = 0 \qquad\qquad S = 0, \bar{S} = 1$$

Pursuing the analogy further, we can introduce operations on switches to correspond to the operations we can perform on propositions. 1) We can couple another switch

$\bar{S}$ to switch S in such a way that $\bar{S}$ is open whenever S is closed, and vice versa. The linkage of the states of these switches is then shown in this table:

S	$\bar{S}$
1	0
0	1

This table is like the truth table for the negation of a propositional form. Let us call switch $\bar{S}$ the complement of switch S.

2) We can control the current in the appliance by a combination of two switches in parallel. If the two switches are called S and T, let us designate the parallel combination by $S + T$. It behaves like a single switch that may be open or closed. If S and T are both closed, current flows through the appliance, so $S + T$ is closed. $S + T$ is also closed if S is closed and T is open, or if S is open and T is closed. If

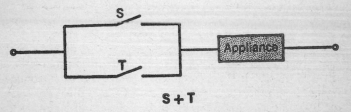

S + T

both S and T are open, then no current flows through the appliance. In this case, $S + T$ is open. The way the state of $S + T$ depends on the states of S and T is shown in this table:

S	T	$S + T$
1	1	1
1	0	1
0	1	1
0	0	0

This table is like the truth table for the disjunction of two propositions.

3) Two switches S and T can be put into the circuit in series. Let us designate the series combination by ST. It, too, behaves like a single switch. ST is closed if and only

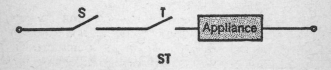

ST

if both S and T are closed. The way the state of ST depends on the states of S and T is shown in this table:

S	T	ST
1	1	1
1	0	0
0	1	0
0	0	0

This table is like the truth table for the conjunction of two propositions.

The three tables show that the resemblance between switches and the truth values of propositions is not accidental. Switches, with the three operations defined above, constitute a two-valued Boolean algebra. Hence switching circuits can be analyzed by algebraic methods. This fact was first discovered by Claude E. Shannon in 1938.

Designing a Circuit

An immediate consequence of Shannon's discovery is that it is possible to use the techniques of Boolean algebra for designing a switching circuit that must satisfy special requirements. The procedure is to set up a "truth table" showing the characteristics we want the circuit to have. Then, using the methods of the last chapter, we can get a formula for the circuit. In the formula, every plus sign represents a parallel connection, every multiplication sign represents a series connection, and every bar over the name of a switch represents taking its complement.

As an example, let us solve the following common switching problem: A light for a flight of stairs is to be controlled by two switches. One of them, S, is upstairs. The other one, T, is downstairs. We want to be able to turn the light on or off by using either switch. Let X stand for the desired switching circuit. Each switch has two states that we designate by 1 and 0. Assume that the light is on, and hence $X = 1$, when each switch is in the state 1. Changing the state of either switch should turn the light off. Hence $X = 0$ when $S = 1$ and $T = 0$, or when $S = 0$ and $T = 1$. Another change in state of a single switch should turn the light on again. Hence $X = 1$ when $S = T = 0$. The truth table for X therefore has this form:

S	T	X
1	1	1
1	0	0
0	1	0
0	0	1

Applying the procedure described on page 109, we find $X = ST + \bar{S}\bar{T}$. The circuit described by this formula is shown in the diagram below:

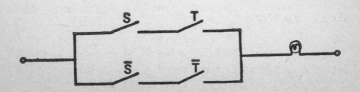

The diagram above does not show the linkage between S and $\bar{S}$ and between T and $\bar{T}$. There is another diagram for the same circuit that does:

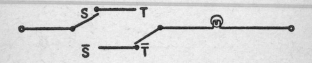

Simplifying a Circuit

Boolean algebra gives the engineer a powerful tool for simplifying a circuit. After a circuit is represented symbolically by an algebraic expression, the rules of Boolean algebra can be used to find equivalent expressions. Each of these equivalent expressions represents a circuit that can take the place of the original one. For example, let us try to simplify the circuit shown in the diagram below.

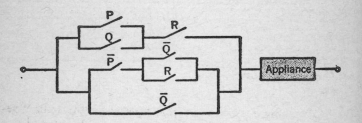

The expression for this circuit is
$(P + Q)R + [\bar{P}(\bar{Q} + R) + \bar{Q}]$. This expression can be transformed as follows:

$(P + Q)R + [\bar{P}(\bar{Q} + R) + \bar{Q}]$

$$= PR + QR + \bar{P}\bar{Q} + \bar{P}R + \bar{Q}$$
$$= (PR + \bar{P}R) + QR + \bar{Q} + \bar{P}Q$$
$$= R(P + \bar{P}) + QR + \bar{Q}(1 + \bar{P})$$
$$= R \cdot 1 + QR + \bar{Q} \cdot 1$$
$$= R(1 + Q) + \bar{Q}$$
$$= R \cdot 1 + \bar{Q} = R + \bar{Q}.$$

Notice that, in carrying out these transformations, we used certain rules, such as the distributive law, the associative laws, the commutative laws, and the law of 1, that are common to Boolean algebra and the algebra of numbers. But we also used some special rules of Boolean algebra, such as $X + \bar{X} = 1$, and $1 + X = 1$. The results of the algebraic computation show that the original circuit can be replaced by the following much simpler one:

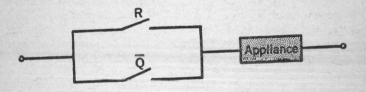

Circuits and Logic

Switching circuits and propositions have the same algebra. It is the two-valued Boolean algebra. Because of this fact, any expression in the algebra may be given two different interpretations. It may be interpreted as a compound switch built out of elementary switches, or it may be interpreted as a compound proposition built out of elementary propositions. For example, the expression $s\ t$ represents equally well the conjunction of two propositions s and t, or a series combination of two switches s and t. Because of this double interpretation that is possible, the algebraic expressions set up a correspondence between the elements of the system of switching circuits and the elements of the system of propositional forms. We have used this correspondence in one direction by employing symbolic logic to solve circuit problems. We can also use it in the opposite direction by employing circuits to solve logical problems. For example, the truth table of a compound propositional form can be represented by a switching circuit. If we use a meter as the appliance in the circuit, then it will indicate automatically the truth value of the form for each choice of truth values for the variables in it. To show that a variable *s* is given the truth value 1, simply close the corresponding switch *s*. To show that the variable *s* is being given the truth value 0, leave the switch *s* open. The truth value of the compound proposition will be 1 if and only if the meter shows the presence of current. The circuits needed for

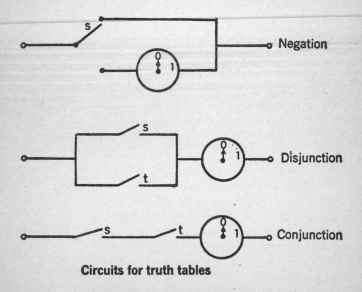

Circuits for truth tables

negation, disjunction, and conjunction are immediately obvious, and are shown above. But if switching circuits can solve logical problems, it means that we can use them to do some of our thinking. This is the reason why switching circuits, or their electronic equivalents, are the materials from which the control systems of thinking machines are built.

CHAPTER 11

Electronic Computers

Gates

A SWITCH is an electrical gate placed across the path of an electric current. When the switch is closed, the gate is open, and current can pass through. When the switch is open, the gate is closed and the current is stopped. The parallel and series combinations of switches described in the preceding chapter are gates of a special kind. Two switches in parallel form what is called an *or* gate, because they permit current to flow through only if one *or* the other switch is closed. Two switches in series form what is called an *and* gate, because they permit current to flow through only if one switch *and* the other switch are closed.

We have talked about the opening and closing of switches without considering how they are opened and closed. One way of opening and closing switches is to operate them electrically, in the device known as a *relay*. In a relay, the moving arm of a switch is adjacent to the iron core of an electromagnet. When current flows through the coil of the electromagnet, the core is magnetized and pulls the switch closed. When the current stops, the core ceases being a magnet. Then the arm of the switch is released, and a spring pulls it back, so that the switch is opened. The effect of the relay is that a current in one circuit is used to control the current in another circuit. Let us call the current in the electromagnet the *input,* and the current in the line containing the switch the *output.* Denote a flow of current by 1, and the absence of current by 0. Then the behavior of a single relay-operated switch can be

124

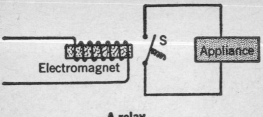

A relay

described in these terms: If the input is 1, the output is 1; while if the input is 0, the output is 0.

If two switches *A* and *B* are relay-operated, and are in parallel to form an *or* gate, the behavior of the *or* gate can be described in these terms: If the input to either *A or B* is 1, then the output is 1. Otherwise the output is 0. Here is another way of stating this fact: The *or* gate produces the output by *adding* the inputs according to the rules of the two-valued Boolean algebra.

If *A* and *B* are in series to form an *and* gate, the behavior of the *and* gate may be described as follows: If the input to *A and B* is 1, then the output is 1. Otherwise the output is 0. Here is an equivalent formulation of this statement: The *and* gate produces the output by *multiplying* the inputs according to the rules of the two-valued Boolean algebra.

A relay can also be wired so that the switch it operates is opened when the arm is pulled by the electromagnet, and is closed when the arm is released. In this case, an input of 1 produces an output of 0, and vice versa. A relay operating in this way is called an *inverter*. The behavior of an *inverter,* too, can be described in the language of Boolean algebra: The output of an *inverter* is the *complement* of the input.

The *or* gate, the *and* gate, and the *inverter* are the electrical analogues of union, intersection, and complementation of classes, and of disjunction, conjunction, and negation of propositions. They are the hardware embodiment of the logical concepts denoted by the words *or, and,* and *not.*

With these gates supplying the basic operations of addition, multiplication, and complementation, currents become the elements of a Boolean algebra.

Electronic Gates

There are electronic components made of combinations of tubes, resistors, etc., that serve the same functions as the relay-operated gates. They, too, will be referred to by the names *or gate, and gate,* and *inverter.* A simplified schematic diagram for each of these components is shown below. We shall not discuss how they work, because such a discussion involves electronic details that go beyond the

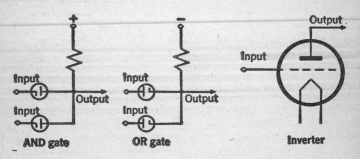

scope of this book. However, we are interested here in how they are used. Our first goal in this chapter is to see how appropriate combinations of these electronic components can be put together to form an electronic computer capable of doing such things as adding or multiplying numbers.

In diagrams of the logical organization of an electronic computer, a special symbol is used for each of these three electronic components. These symbols are shown below alongside diagrams of the analogous switching circuits. (In the switching diagrams, for the sake of simplicity, the electromagnet that operates each switch is omitted.) The *and* gate and the *or* gate both have two inputs and one output. Using Boolean algebra notation, if the inputs are A and B, then the output of the *and* gate is AB, and the output of the *or* gate is $A + B$. The inverter has one input, A, and its output is $\bar{A}$.

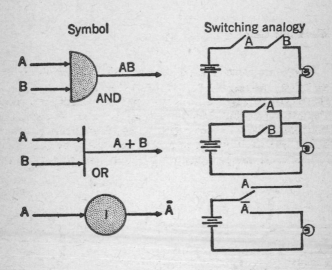

Numbers Written by Currents

The current in a wire may be either *on* or *off*. This two-valued nature of the state of the current permits it to be used to represent a bit in a binary numeral. If we use a separate wire for each bit, then the whole numeral can be expressed by the state of the currents in them. For example, suppose we have four wires side by side, from left to right, with the state of the current in these wires as follows: on—off—on—off. Then these states represent the binary numeral 1010, which stands for the number *ten*.

When we use decimal numerals, we refer to the position

of the first digit on the right as the *units* column. The second digit is in the *tens* column, the third digit is in the *hundreds* column, and so on. Similarly, we shall refer to positions from right to left in a binary numeral as the *units* column, the *twos* column, the *fours* column, etc.

Designing an Electronic Adding Machine

We are now ready to deal with the problem of designing an electronic circuit that is capable of doing addition of numbers. Let us begin by observing the procedure of a person who adds two numbers written in binary notation. First he writes the numbers one under the other. Then he adds the columns, one at a time, starting with the units column. The addition of the units column differs in an important way from the addition of every other column. In the units column, there are only *two* bits to add. In every other column there are *three* bits to add. Two of them are the bits that appear in the addends in that column. The third bit is the *carry* from the addition in the column to the right. This carry may be a 1 or a 0. (The carry is 0 when the sum of the bits added is 0 or 1. The carry is 1 when the sum is 10 or 11.) So, to carry out addition electronically, we need two different kinds of devices. We need one that can add *two* bits and then produce separately the bit that is put down in the sum and the bit that is to be carried. Such a device is called a *half adder*. We also need a device that can add *three* bits, and produce separately the bit for the sum and the carry. This device is known as a *full adder*. A half adder would suffice to add the bits in the units column. A full adder would be needed for each of the other columns.

The Half Adder

A half adder has two inputs. These are the bits in the units column of the addends. Let us call these bits A and B. The half adder also has two outputs, the bit that goes into the sum, and the bit that is carried. Let us call these S and C respectively. The values of S and C for different values of A and B are shown in the table below:

A	B	S	C
1	1	0	1
1	0	1	0
0	1	1	0
0	0	0	0

What we really have here is a truth table for S and C. Using the procedure described on page 109, we can get from these truth tables a formula for S and a formula for C:

$$S = \bar{A}B + A\bar{B}; \qquad C = AB.$$

These formulas give us instructions for making a circuit that will work as a half adder. Every bar in the formulas indicates the use of an inverter. Every multiplication sign indicates the use of an *and* gate. Every plus sign indicates the use of an *or* gate. To produce the output S, we proceed as follows: Use an inverter to change A into $\bar{A}$. Use an inverter to change B into $\bar{B}$. Use an *and* gate to multiply $\bar{A}$ and B, producing the product $\bar{A}B$. Use an *and* gate to multiply A and $\bar{B}$, producing the product $A\bar{B}$. Then use an *or* gate to add $\bar{A}B$ and $A\bar{B}$, producing S. To produce the output C, we need only an *and* gate to multiply A and B. The circuit for the half adder is shown in the diagram below.

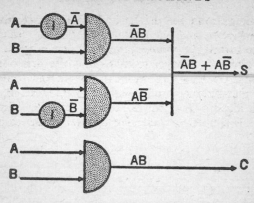

Circuit for half adder

The formulas for S and C given above are not the only ones that fit the truth tables for S and C. There are others that we can get by manipulating these formulas according to the rules of Boolean algebra. Each set of formulas obtained in this way is the design for another circuit that can do the work of a half adder. For example, on page 87 we showed that the expression $\bar{A}B + A\bar{B}$ is equivalent to $(A + B)\bar{C}$. So another formula for S is $S = (A + B)\bar{C}$. This formula gives us another circuit for producing S. In this circuit, an inverter is used to produce $\bar{C}$ from C. An *or* gate is used to add A and B. Then an *and* gate is used to multiply $A + B$ by $\bar{C}$. The new circuit for the half adder is shown below.

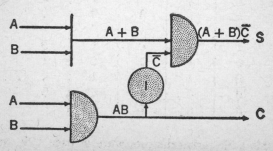

Simplified circuit for half adder

The first circuit for the half adder used two inverters, three *and* gates, and one *or* gate. The second circuit uses only one inverter, two *and* gates, and one *or* gate. So the second circuit is cheaper to make than the first one. This shows that Boolean algebra has a dollars and cents value for the manufacturers of electronic computers. By using Boolean algebra, they can sometimes replace a circuit by one that is simpler and cheaper and serves the same purpose.

The Full Adder

A full adder has three inputs. Two of them are the bits of the addends that appear in the column being added. Let us call them A and B. The third one is the carry from the addition of the next column to the right. Let us call this bit C. The full adder has two outputs, the bit that goes into the sum, and the bit that is carried. Let us call these S and D respectively. The values of S and D for different values of $A, B,$ and C are shown in this table:

A	B	C	S	D
1	1	1	1	1
1	1	0	0	1
1	0	1	0	1
1	0	0	1	0
0	1	1	0	1
0	1	0	1	0
0	0	1	1	0
0	0	0	0	0

From this table, using the procedure of page 109, we get these formulas for S and D: $S = ABC + \bar{A}\bar{B}C + \bar{A}B\bar{C} +$

$\bar{A}BC. D = ABC + AB\bar{C} + A\bar{B}C + \bar{A}BC$. Now, using the rules of Boolean algebra, we modify these formulas as follows:

$$S = ABC + A\bar{B}\bar{C} + \bar{A}B\bar{C} + \bar{A}\bar{B}C$$
$$= (ABC + \bar{A}\bar{B}C) + (\bar{A}B\bar{C} + A\bar{B}\bar{C})$$
$$= (AB + \bar{A}\bar{B})C + (\bar{A}B + A\bar{B})\bar{C}$$

On page 88 we found that $AB + \bar{A}\bar{B} = \overline{\bar{A}B + A\bar{B}}$. Substituting the latter expression for $AB + \bar{A}\bar{B}$, we get

$$S = (\overline{\bar{A}B + A\bar{B}})C + (\bar{A}B + A\bar{B})\bar{C}.$$

This may look like a more complicated expression for S, but it has an important advantage over the earlier one. It expresses S in terms of $\bar{A}B + A\bar{B}$ and C. The former is the *sum* output of a half adder operating on A and B, while the latter is the *carry* output from the addition of the preceding column. This version of the formula permits us to incorporate a half adder as a unit in the design of a full adder.

$$D = ABC + AB\bar{C} + A\bar{B}C + \bar{A}BC$$
$$= (\bar{A}BC + A\bar{B}C) + (ABC + AB\bar{C})$$
$$= (\bar{A}B + A\bar{B})C + AB(C + \bar{C})$$
$$= (\bar{A}B + A\bar{B})C + AB(1)$$

So $$D = (\bar{A}B + A\bar{B})C + AB.$$

This formula for D expresses it in terms of $\bar{A}B + A\bar{B}$, AB, and C. The first of these is the *sum* output of a half adder operating on A and B. The second is the *carry* output of the same half adder. The third is the *carry* output from the addition of the preceding column. So we can also use a half

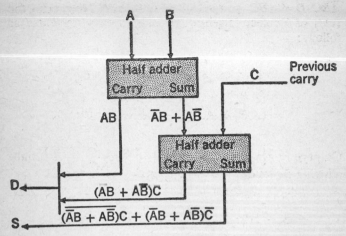

Full adder made with two half adders and an OR

adder as a unit in the part of the circuit that produces D. Taking our cue from these formulas, we can build a full adder out of two half adders, as shown in the diagram.

A Calculator with a Heart Beat

Just as there are many ways of putting *and* gates, *or* gates, and *inverters* together to form a half adder, there are many ways of putting half adders and adders together to form a calculator. To give a specific example, we shall examine some of the details of the design of a particular machine, the Naval Ordnance Research Calculator (known by its initials as NORC), built for the Navy by the International Business Machines Corporation.

A special feature of the NORC is that it has a "heart" beat. Electrical pulses, generated electronically, beat a regular rhythm throughout the machine. The pulses are generated at the rate of one million per second. There are other pulses that are fed into the machine to represent numbers, instructions, and so on. When the pulses are passed on from one part of the machine to another, they move in step with the rhythm of the heart beat.

The Dynamic Pulse Unit

Another feature of the NORC is its use of a special component known as a Dynamic Pulse Unit, or DPU. A DPU has an input terminal through which it may receive an electrical pulse, and an output terminal through which it may send one out. The chief function of the DPU is to introduce a delay of a microsecond (one millionth of a

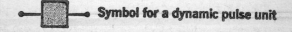

Symbol for a dynamic pulse unit

second) between the input pulse and the output pulse. If it receives a pulse at the moment of one heart beat, it sends one out at the moment of the next heart beat. Otherwise it doesn't send out any pulse at all. The NORC contains about 1500 DPU's.

At each heart beat, a DPU receives a signal through its input terminal. This signal is either the presence or the absence of a pulse. At the next heart beat, it passes on this same signal to its output terminal. There are multitudes of electronic switches in the NORC. By opening or closing the switches in various combinations, different pathways are opened up along which the signal may be routed. A signal can be stored for any number of microseconds in a DPU. To store a signal in a DPU, it is fed into the input terminal of the DPU at the moment of a heart beat. Then, immediately, the output terminal is connected to the input terminal of the same DPU. So, when the DPU transmits the pulse at the next heart beat, it transmits the pulse to itself. In this way the pulse is renewed over and over again every microsecond, until it is switched into some other component. A DPU whose output is joined to its input is said to be in the *circulate* condition.

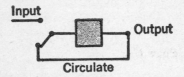

Temporary storage in a DPU

Numbers in the NORC

To write numbers, the NORC uses the compromise system described on page 54. It expresses numbers in terms of decimal digits, but each digit is represented by four bits. The four bits for a digit are expressed as signals along four separate wires. A thirteen-digit number would require 52 bits to represent it. These are accompanied by 12 other bits that serve these additional purposes: 8 bits, standing for 2 digits, indicate the position of the decimal point in the number; 4 bits, standing for one digit, indicate the algebraic sign. So 64 bits altogether represent the number. Two more bits are used for checking purposes. The total of 66 bits constitutes what is called a *number word*.

The position of the decimal point is indicated by means of a simple code. The digit 0, in this code, means that the decimal point is in standard position, that is, to the right of the first digit in the number. A code number between 1 and 30 inclusive indicates that the decimal point is that number of places to the right of standard position. For example, the code number 5 means that the decimal point is five places to the right of standard position. A code number between

70 and 99 inclusive indicates that the decimal point is to the left of standard position. To find out how many places to the left it is, you must subtract the code number from 100. For example, if the code number is 97, the decimal point is three places to the left of standard position.

To show the algebraic sign of the number, the digits 0 and 1 are used. The digit 0 indicates a positive number, and the digit 1 indicates a negative number. Whenever a number is written, the code number for the sign is placed to the left of the digits of the number. The code number for the position of the decimal point is placed to the left of the code number for the sign. According to this scheme, for example, the sequence 08/0/567 123 806 542 9 would represent the number $+ 567{,}123{,}806.5429$.

The NORC Memory

The memory or storage unit of the NORC is a set of tubes like the picture tubes of a television set. The face of each tube is thought of as being divided into little squares. Each square is a *location*. A single bit can be stored in each location. This is done by aiming the electron gun of the tube at the location or at a spot near it. The electron gun sends out a stream of electrons. If the stream strikes the location, it knocks electrons out of the glass there. Electronic engineers call this *digging a hole*. If the stream strikes a spot near a location in which a hole has been dug, it restores the missing electrons. This is called *filling the hole*. The stream is made to *dig* a hole in order to store a 0. It is made to fill the hole in order to store a 1.

There is a conducting surface outside each storage tube, near its face. This surface is used for reading the bits that are stored in the tube. To read the bit stored at a location, the electron stream is aimed at it. If the bit is a 1, there is no hole at that location. The stream now digs a hole there. The digging causes a pulse of current to appear in a wire connected to the conducting surface. So a 1 stored at the location is read as a pulse in the wire. If the bit stored at the location is a 0, there is a hole there. Then the electron stream does no digging there, because the hole is already dug. As a result no pulse appears in the wire from the conducting surface. So a 0 stored at the location is read as the absence of a pulse in the wire.

Taking a Number from Storage

The 64 bits that represent a number can be stored at 64 locations in the storage unit. This combination of bit locations is a *word* location. To take a number out of storage, the wire from each bit location is switched to the input terminal of a separate DPU. At the next heart beat, each bit enters a DPU. Then the DPU's are switched to *circulate*. The number is now stored in the set of 64 DPU's until it is needed. This set of DPU's, used together as a unit, is called a *register*. When two numbers are to be added, each is first stored in a register. Then the numbers are fed from the two registers into the adding unit. In what follows we disregard decimal points and algebraic signs, and consider only the addition of natural numbers.

Moving a Number

Once a number is stored in a register, the machine can make the number move. To make it move, it first arranges the digits of the number in a line. This is done by switching the DPU's so that they form four lines, as shown in the diagram below. Each set of four DPU's that are in a vertical column contains the bits that represent a single digit. The column on the extreme right contains the units digit, the next column contains the tens digit, and so on. In other words, the arrangement of the digits along the four lines matches exactly our usual way of writing a decimal numeral.

Now suppose each of the four lines is lengthened by joining more DPU's to its right hand end. At the first heart beat after that, each DPU passes its bit on to the DPU to its right. The four bits that represent a digit therefore move in unison, one place to the right. At the next heart beat, they

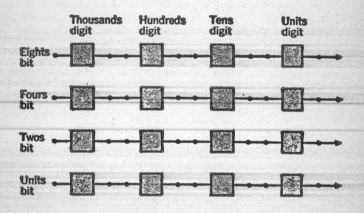

move to the right again. The four rows of bits march to the right, in step with the rhythm of the heart beat, like a column of soldiers on parade.

How the NORC Adds Numbers

To add two numbers, first each is stored in a register. Then their digits are lined up, as described above, and they are moved into an adding unit, one digit at a time. At the moment of a heart beat, the units digits enter the adding unit. The adding unit adds the digits and obtains two digits, one for the sum, and one to carry. At the next heart beat, it passes the sum digit on to the left end of a register, and passes the carry digit on to itself. The carry digit enters the adder at the same time that the tens digits enter. In

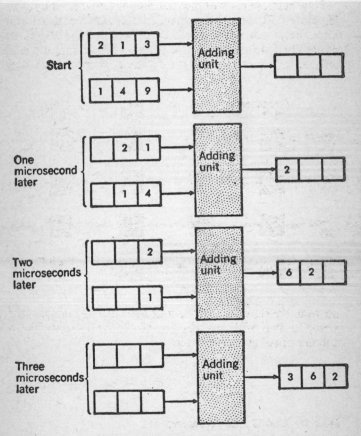

Adding three-digit numbers

this way the adding unit carries from the units column to the tens column just as we do when we add with pencil and paper. Beat by beat, the digits of the two numbers march into the adding unit, and the digits of the sum march out at the other end.

Now let us peek inside the adding unit to see how it produces the sum and carry digits. When two digits enter the adding unit, each digit makes its entrance in the guise of a four-bit binary numeral. We saw on page 128 that two such numerals can be added by a combination of one half adder and three full adders. We can provide for a carry digit that may be 0 or 1 by replacing the half adder

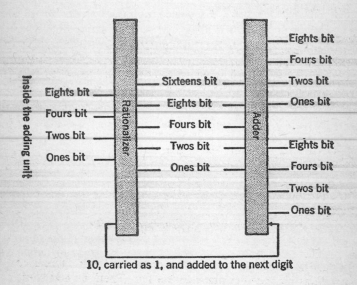

10, carried as 1, and added to the next digit

by a full adder. So a battery of four full adders can take care of the addition of two digits and the carry from the previous addition. Let us use the word *adder* as a brief designation for this battery of full adders. Its output is sometimes a number that is higher than fifteen, and may even be as high as nineteen (9 + 9 + 1). To write a number this high requires five bits. So the sum appears at first as a five-bit numeral. If the sum is ten or higher, it is necessary to decompose the number into two parts. One part is the sum digit that is to be passed on to the register that receives the answer. The other part is the ten which is exchanged for a 1 to be carried. This job of decomposing the sum is carried out by a special unit called a *rationalizer*. The complete adding unit includes a rationalizer as well as an adder.

How the NORC Multiplies

To see how the NORC multiplies numbers, let us first examine the common paper and pencil method of doing multiplication. If we want to multiply 327 by 415, first we multiply 327 by the digits 4, 1, and 5 separately. We

$$
\begin{array}{r}
327 \\
\times\ 415 \\
\hline
1635 \\
327 \\
1308 \\
\hline
135705
\end{array}
$$

Common method of multiplying

write the products one under the other, with successive products shifted one place to the left. Then we add these products. To be prepared to multiply *any* two numbers, we need only know how to 1) multiply by any digit from 0 to 9, 2) arrange the appropriate partial products correctly, and 3) add them. The NORC multiplies numbers in essentially the same way. However, its method differs from the common one in two respects. In the common method of multiplication, we multiply the multiplicand by only those digits that appear in the multiplier. Moreover, we multiply by one digit at a time. The NORC multiplies by all the digits from 0 to 9, and does all these ten multiplications at the same time. Then it *selects* for addition only those products that correspond to digits of the multiplier. So the work of the NORC is made up of four parts: 1) multiply by the digits, 2) select the appropriate products, 3) arrange them, and 4) add them. Let us examine the details of each of these parts.

Multiplying. Multiplying by 1 requires no effort at all, since the product is the same as the multiplicand. To multiply by 2, we make use of a fact we observed on page 35: You can multiply a binary numeral by 2 by shifting each bit one place to the left. The NORC does it in this way: The digits of the multiplicand are lined up in a register, and are then fed, one at a time, into a rationalizer. But the bits that represent the digits are not put into the usual input terminals. Instead they are shifted one place to the left. The units bit is put into the twos terminal, the twos bit is put into the fours terminal, and so on. This automatically doubles each digit. Meanwhile, the rationalizer decomposes the result into a single digit and a carry. The single digit emerges from the output of the rationalizer. The carry is joined to the units input

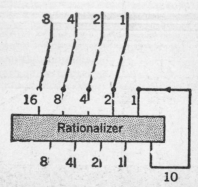

A rationalizer used to multiply by 2

terminal of the rationalizer. Then it is combined with double the next digit that enters the rationalizer. In this way the modified rationalizer doubles a number by dou-

bling its digits, one after another, and carrying where necessary, just as we do in mental multiplication.

To multiply a number by 3, the NORC is guided by
the distributive law: $3N = (2 + 1) N = 2N + 1N$. It
multiplies a number by 3 by doubling the number and
then adding the result to the original number. To multiply
a number by 4, it doubles the number, and then doubles
the result.

To multiply a number by 5, the NORC multiplies it
by ten, and then divides by two. As we saw on page 35,
you can multiply a decimal number by ten by moving each
digit one place to the left. In the NORC, the digits of a
number are lined up in a register, and then are fed into
the calculating units one digit at a time. The first digit
to enter is the units digit. Then the tens digit enters, and
so on. There is a special time reserved for the entry of
each digit. If the entry digits are all delayed for the interval
between two successive heart beats, then the units digit
enters at the time reserved for the tens digit, the tens digit
enters at the time reserved for the hundreds digit, and so

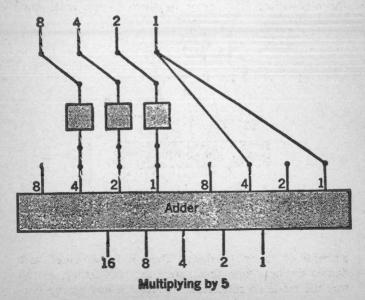

Multiplying by 5

on. It is as if all the digits had been shifted one place to the left in the register. The result is that the number has been multiplied by ten. Dividing by two is the opposite of multiplying by two, and is accomplished by shifting one place to the right the bits that represent each digit. The NORC applies these two techniques simultaneously on the twos bit, the fours bit, and the eights bit of each digit, as they are fed into an adder. To multiply the units bit by 5, it simply feeds it into both the units and fours terminal, so that a one is converted into one plus four. The connections for multiplying a number by 5 are shown in the diagram.

To multiply a number by 6, the NORC first multiplies it by 3, and then doubles the result. To multiply a number by 7, it multiplies the number separately by 5 and 2, and

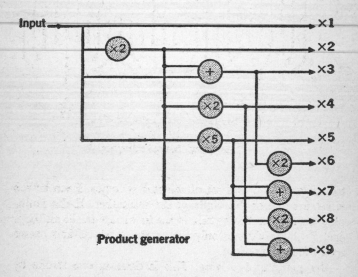

Product generator

then adds the products. To multiply by 8, it doubles the result of multiplying by 4. To multiply by 9, it first multiplies by 4 and 5 separately, and then adds the products.

All the multiplications are carried out in one unit called

the *product generator*. A diagram of the product generator is shown above.

Selecting. As all nine products emerge from the genera-

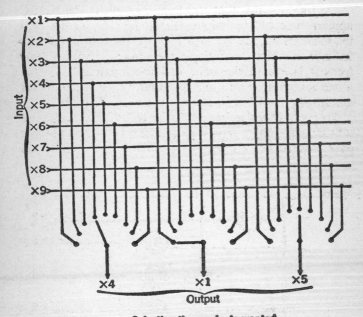

Selecting the products wanted

tor, they are fed to a set of selector switches. Each switch is set for one of the digits of the multiplier. If the multiplier digit is 0, the switch is set to an *off* position. Thus each switch picks out only one of the products and passes it on as its own output.

Arranging and Adding. This is done at one stroke by feeding the outputs of the selector switches into components joined in series as shown in the diagram. The product by the digit furthest to the left is fed into a DPU, while the rest are fed into adding units. Each of these units introduces a delay of one microsecond. The delay has the effect of shifting successive partial products one place to the left at the same time that they are being added.

Putting all these complex connections together, we get

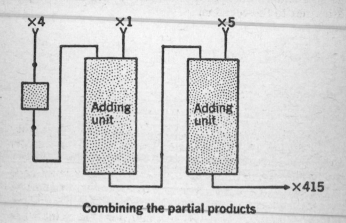

Combining the partial products

the NORC *multiplier*. When two numbers are multiplied, they are fed from registers into the multiplier. Five microseconds after the multiplicand begins moving into the multiplier, the product begins to emerge into another register.

Numbers for Places

Suppose a number is stored in the NORC's memory, and we want the machine to transfer this number from storage to a register. Then we must instruct the machine to connect a register to certain storage locations. The instructions must describe the locations in a language that the machine can "understand." This language takes the form of numbers. A number is assigned to each location, just as we assign street numbers and house numbers to the locations at which we live. The number assigned to a location is called its *address*. The machine is wired so that when the address of a location is fed into the machine as part of its instructions, the appropriate switches are closed to join a register to this location.

Numbers for Instructions

The instructions given to the NORC also tell it what to do. It may be told to add two numbers, or to multiply them, etc. These instructions, too, must be given in a language that the machine can understand. A number code is used for this purpose, too. For example, if two numbers drawn from storage are called A and B, the instruction number 20 means, "Find $A + B$ and store the result." The instruction number 23 means, "Find $A - B$, change the sign of the answer, and store the result."

By means of this code, all instructions to the machine can be written out as a sequence of digits. Sixteen digits, or 64 bits, are used. Two additional bits are used for checking purposes. The total of 64 bits is called an *instruction word*. Here is part of an instruction word, and its translation into English:

Instruction: . . . 20/0168/0341/0649
Meaning: Take the number in storage location 168, add
          to it the number in storage location 341, and
          store the result in storage location 649.

An important consequence of using a number code for instructions is that *instructions* can be stored in the machine's memory unit. This makes it possible to tell the machine to perform certain operations, and then go to a certain storage address to find out what to do next.

Input and Output

To put information into storage, it is first entered on a punch card. This is done on a machine that has a keyboard resembling that of a typewriter. When the operator strikes the appropriate keys, holes are punched in a card to express the information in the punch card code. From the punch card, the information is transferred to magnetic tape.

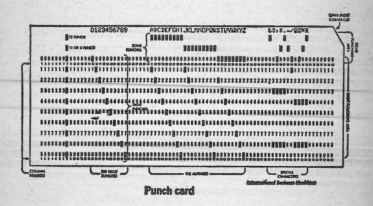

Punch card

It is recorded electrically on the tape in the form of bits. Each bit takes the form of the presence or the absence of a magnetized spot on the tape, just as each bit in the memory tube takes the form of the presence or absence of a charged spot. From the tape, the information is transferred into a register, and from the register, it is fed into storage. To get the output of the machine in printed form, this procedure is reversed. Information is moved from storage to a register, and from there to a tape. From the tape it is transferred to a punch card, from which it can be read off by a printer.

The machine has one more avenue of contact with its operator. There is a console with switches and indicators.

By means of the switches, the operator can give and modify instructions. Through the indicators, she sees what the machine is doing at each step.

Speed

Because it works to the rhythm of its heart beat, the NORC works very fast. It can add two thirteen-digit numbers in fifteen microseconds. At this speed, it can do in one second as many calculations as a man working with pencil and paper can do in a week. As a result, calculations that are "impossible" if done by hand, simply because they would take too long to be practical, become practical, and hence possible, if done by machine.

CHAPTER 12

Thinking Machines and the Brain

Machines That Behave Like Brains

AUTOMATIC calculating machines have been called thinking machines because they behave in many ways like a brain. They can carry out numerical calculations. These range in difficulty and complexity from simple counting to solving differential equations. They can receive and follow instructions. They have memories, in which they can store information for future use. Because they are equipped with *and, or* and *not* components, they can carry out the logical operations we call deductive reasoning.

The combination of all these qualities gives the machines another brain-like property. They can make comparisons, and then, on the basis of what they observe, choose among alternative courses of action. A checker-playing machine, for example, can calculate ahead, for several moves, the consequences of each move it may make. Then, using fixed rules that are part of its instructions, it evaluates the different possible moves, and chooses the one that is "best" according to its built-in standards of judgment.

A recent improvement has been the design of machines that can learn from their experience. One of these is the machine that plays checkers. In its first games, it is guided by its original instructions. As it plays, it stores a record of all its moves in its memory. Then, after a certain number of games have been played, it evaluates its moves in terms of their actual consequences. Then it modifies its own instructions to take its past experience into account. Tactics that did not work out so well are discarded. Tactics that led most often to victory are given greater emphasis. By repeatedly revising its instructions the machine steadily perfects its game.

The Brain Is Like a Machine

Since it seems to make sense to compare a calculating machine to the brain, it is natural to try to turn the comparison around. Is the brain like a calculating machine? We find that in some respects it is. A digital calculating machine is a complex electrical network built up out of a large number of units. The most basic unit is the vacuum tube, or its modern substitute, the transistor. There are also other units built out of the basic units. These include such components as DPU's, *and* gates, *or* gates, and inverters. The brain is also a complex electrical network built up out of a large number of units. The basic unit in the brain is the *nerve cell*. The behavior of many nerve cells is something like that of a DPU. If they are stimulated by a nerve impulse from another cell, they send out a nerve impulse of their own. Some nerve cells will act when stimulated by any one of several other cells. These cells behave like *or* gates. Others will act only when stimulated by all of a group of other cells. These behave like *and* gates. In these aspects of its behavior, the brain seems to work like a digital computer. However, it is possible, too, that the action of a nerve cell depends on the spatial arrangement of the cells that are joined to it, and the position of a cell that sends it an impulse. Nerve impulses, and chemical and physical stimuli to nerve cells seem to add up to a total stimulus. In this respect, the behavior of the brain is like that of an analog computer. So the brain, to the extent that it is like a calculating machine, seems to be one of mixed type, part digital and part analog.

Brain Versus Machine

How do the brain and the machine compare in complexity and efficiency as pieces of thinking apparatus? We can get a crude answer to this question from certain known facts about the brain and machines. We can use as an index of relative complexity the ratio of the number of unit actions that can be performed by equal volumes of each in equal times. This can be calculated from the ratio of the volumes of the basic units in each, and the ratio of their speeds. A neuron is about one billion times smaller than the basic unit of a calculating machine, and it is about one hundred thousand times slower in its action. Dividing these two figures gives us the desired index. Nerve tissue is about ten thousand times more efficient than electronic hardware.

An aspect of the brain's greater complexity is the great size of its memory capacity. A large modern computer has a memory capacity of one million bits. The memory capacity of the brain has been estimated at 280 billion billion bits. So the brain's memory capacity is 280 million million times as great as that of any existing machine.

The Brain's Memory Unit

In order to give an electronic computer adequate memory capacity, engineers have found it necessary to give the computer a separate memory unit. In order to make this unit efficient, they have found it necessary to build it out of components that are different from the basic active units in the logic and arithmetic sections of the machine. In the NORC, for example, the basic memory unit is a charge on the face of a television tube, rather than a DPU. These facts suggest an interesting series of questions about the brain. Does the brain have a separate memory unit? If it does, where is it? What are the basic units of which it is composed? Experience with electronic computers suggests the possible direction in which answers to these questions may be found. Because the brain has such a great memory capacity, it seems reasonable to assume that, as in the case of machines, the basic memory unit is different from the basic active unit, the nerve cell. For example, the basic stuff of which the memory is composed might be the connections between the nerve cells, rather than the cells themselves. This and other suggestions are being investigated by students of the nervous system.

Toward Better Understanding

Comparisons between the brain and electronic computers are not idle speculations. They are a necessary part of the scientific study of both. These comparisons have already shown themselves to be useful. When the late John von Neumann and his co-workers were designing the computer known as the JONIAC, they deliberately tried to imitate in it some of the known characteristics of the brain. On the other hand, investigators studying the functioning of the brain follow lines of investigation suggested by our knowledge about computers. Neurology and the theory of computers are separate branches of science. But they run parallel to each other to a certain extent, and advances in one field stimulate advances in the other. One of the truly exciting prospects arising from this relationship is that, the more we develop computers, the better we shall understand them. And the better we understand our computers, the better we shall understand ourselves.

Bibliography

Adler, Irving, *Magic House of Numbers,* The John Day Company, New York, N. Y.; The New American Library, New York, N. Y. For a simple introduction to the binary scale.

Adler, Irving, *The New Mathematics,* The John Day Company, New York, N. Y.; The New American Library, New York, N. Y. A popular introduction to algebraic structures.

Boole, George, *An Investigation of the Laws of Thought,* Dover Publications, Inc., New York, N. Y. The pioneer work on Boolean algebra. Mainly of historical interest.

Carroll, Lewis, *Symbolic Logic and the Game of Logic,* Dover Publications, Inc., New York, N. Y. Has a large collection of amusing, logical problems.

Eckert, W. J., and Jones, Rebecca, *Faster, Faster,* McGraw-Hill Book Company, New York, N. Y. A popular description of the NORC.

Gorn, Saul, and Manheimer, Wallace, *The Electronic Brain and What It Can Do,* Science Research Associates, Inc., Chicago, Ill. A fine popular pamphlet.

Langer, Susanne K., *An Introduction to Symbolic Logic,* Dover Publications, Inc., New York, N. Y. An excellent textbook.

Von Neumann, John, *The Computer and the Brain,* Yale University Press, New Haven, Conn. Notes for a popular lecture.

Index

157

SIGNET and MENTOR Books of Related Interest

Magic House of Numbers *by Irving Adler*
Mathematical curiosities, riddles, tricks, and games that teach the basic principles of arithmetic.
(#KD374—50¢)

The New Mathematics *by Irving Adler*
The first book to explain—in simple, uncomplicated language—the fundamental concepts of the revolutionary developments in modern mathematics.
(#P2099—60¢)

Mathematics In Everyday Things *by William C. Vergara*
In fascinating question and answer form, and illustrated with diagrams, this book shows how the basic principles of mathematics are applied to hundreds of scientific problems.
(#P2098—60¢)

Mathematics In Fun and In Earnest *by Nathan Court*
An outstanding geometrician writes of the philosophic depths, delights, and practical utility of the science of mathematics.
(#MD344—50¢)

One Two Three . . . Infinity *by George Gamow*
Current facts and speculations of science presented by a leading physicist.
(#MD97—50¢)

The ABC of Relativity *by Bertrand Russell*
A clear, penetrating explanation of Einstein's theories and their effect on the world.
(#MD258—50¢)

Electronics for Everyone (revised and expanded) *by Monroe Upton*
This easy-to-read, authoritative book helps you understand today's wonders in the field of electricity, and forecasts the exciting future of science. More than 100 practical drawings.
(#KD351—50¢)